Tony Morrison

Animal Migration

illustrated by Pat Oxenham

Hamlyn · London
Sun Books · Melbourne

FOREWORD

Migrations have been observed and recorded by philosophers and chroniclers for many centuries, and yet they remain one of our most intriguing and unsolved mysteries. Early reports came from travellers and explorers, but it is only with the advancement of scientific techniques and the ease of world-wide travel that today we have begun to understand what migrations really are and how and why they occur.

There is no simple definition for the term migration, but, for the purpose of this book, I have used the generally accepted interpretation which limits the use of the term to one or two-way, clearly directional movements. To provide comparisons, some of the borderline cases are included, and so the extraordinary suicidal treks of lemmings and Springboks are seen alongside the shorter, more obscure journeys made in the world of simple animals.

Research has substantiated a few of the theories of migration, but at the same time it has given us more problems to solve. How, for example, does the Arctic Tern manage to fly more than 20,000 miles in a year from the Arctic circle to the distant southern oceans and back again? And how can young Cuckoos find their way south from Europe, when the adults leave them to be raised by non-migratory foster parents.

To find the answers many fields of science have been involved, and some principles of migratory behaviour are now understood, but others still exist only in the realm of speculation. It is at this stage that the enquiring mind of every man has a chance to challenge the disciplined approach of the specialist. The mystery of migration is something that has fascinated all kinds of people through the ages and surely will continue to do so.

T.M.

Published by The Hamlyn Publishing Group Limited
London . New York . Sydney . Toronto .
Hamlyn House, Feltham, Middlesex, England
In association with Sun Books Pty. Ltd. Melbourne

ISBN 0 600 00136 9
Photoset by BAS Printers Limited, Wallop, Hampshire
Colour separations by Schwitter Limited, Zurich
Printed in Holland by Smeets, Weert

CONTENTS

4   Introduction
8   Possible reasons for migration
14   Evolution of migratory behaviour
18   What is migration?
32   Introduction to migratory animals
40   Migration of birds
114   Migration of reptiles and amphibians
118   Migration of fishes
130   Migration of invertebrates
154   Applications of modern research
156   Books to read
156   Places to visit
157   Index

INTRODUCTION

When animals move across the face of the Earth, sometimes making journeys of immense length, their behaviour is generally described as migratory. Even in these days when we ourselves are busily moving from place to place, there is something quite romantic about the travels of the migrants which visit our shores, and in fact the great ornithological competition to hear the first Cuckoo (*Cuculus canorus*) in Britain always seems to generate a barrage of correspondence in the daily papers. As Swallows (*Hirundo rustica*) and Swifts (*Apus apus*) line the telephone wires, waiting for some unheard starter's signal to send them on a long race south, we are hardly aware of their presence; but once they have gone there are a few days when the sky is empty, the time when perhaps we are most conscious that they have been with us.

Animals and their migrations have become part of our folklore. A Salmon (*Salmo salar*) leaping in a turbulent Scottish stream has featured on countless calendars and postcards, and the White Stork (*Ciconia ciconia*) has the reputation in many countries of providing the best baby delivery service. Lemmings with their powerfully motivated suicidal marches are quoted by politicians and philosophers, who predict the doomsday of mankind.

For the primitive societies annual migrations of some animals have a far stronger meaning. As game herds move through tribal territory, year after year, people are assured of food and it is disastrous if the beasts fail to appear. Climatic changes can upset the general pattern, and such variations are recognized by the tribal elders or witch-doctors, who use the knowledge to retain power. For the primitive peoples in the forests of New Guinea and South America, survival depends on an association with the wildlife. These people know the time of year when they can expect large mammals near the rivers or flocks of wildfowl on forest lagoons. Just as careful observation of the fauna is vital to these tribes today, so it was to early man who watched migrations in much the same way, as we can see from his cave art.

The passage of birds and mammals was probably recognized by prehistoric man as long ago as 20,000 years. In

Europe and parts of Africa, rock carvings and cave paintings, many of which have survived in perfect condition, illustrate faunal types most important to the early hunter. More recently our major religious works contain references to animal migrations. In the Old Testament plagues of locusts are mentioned, and the Prophet Jeremiah recorded the flight of the bee-eaters, those tiny, brilliant birds known today from Africa to Australia. Some temperate zone species of bee-

In Sweden people watch anxiously for the arrival of the Cranes.

eater migrate, and their movements are familiar to people in the Mediterranean countries – very occasionally bee-eaters visit Britain.

Other famous chroniclers made observations: Aristotle speculated on the reasons for migration, and noted the seasons when Quail (*Coturnix coturnix*) and Cranes (*Megalornis grus*) arrived. In the Iliad, the Trojan armies were likened to a company of Cranes. Ancient books in Sanskrit or early Scandinavian poems leave no doubt that migrations were watched with great fascination by our ancestors.

As man progressed and his interest in science and en-

Early man all over the world noticed animals on the move and depicted them in his primitive art.

Some early explorers like Captain Cook noticed mass migrations of insects.

vironment grew, we find that records of unusual happenings in the animal world were described in detail. The sudden appearance of large swarms of butterflies caught the imagination of many writers: Captain Cook described the harbour of Rio de Janeiro when he was there in December 1768 and on one occasion said that the air was full of butterflies 'chiefly of one sort, but in such numbers that thousands were in view in every direction'. Later still we have even more detailed information on migrations from naturalists of fame, including Darwin. Studies and observation techniques have progressed and now follow many different and sophisticated lines of research. Ringing or banding of birds which began in the last century with simple marking, such as tying coloured cotton to the legs or cutting the toes of swifts, has increased to the point when many millions of birds now carry some form of identification, and reports are collated in many countries.

POSSIBLE REASONS FOR MIGRATION

In spite of very rapid advances made during the past few years in the study of migration, many of the reasons for this behaviour remain hypothetical. As often happens in a developing science, some of the facts seem to fit one set of circumstances, while for another set there seems to be no correlation. Not all animals migrate long distances; some appear to move in one direction only; and some travel along the same route year after year with such precision that it is almost possible to set a clock by their passing. In much of the northern hemisphere we are accustomed to seeing the arrival and departure of many species of birds in spring and autumn, and occasionally there are irruptions of some species, seldom recorded in normal periods. Late in 1970, large numbers of Waxwings (*Bombycilla garrulus*) were reported from the eastern counties of Britain, and their appearance was related to an early onset of winter in their native Europe.

It is generally believed that there is frequently a close

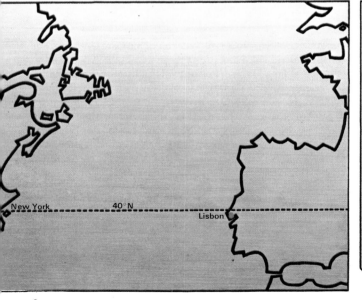

New York   40° N   Lisbon

general direction of animal movement at onset of cold weather

Wilson's Phalaropes migrate in search of warmth and food.

relationship between the availability of food and the path
followed by the migrants. When this is the case the animals
seem to be following a course that takes them into richer
life zones. Certainly the Swifts and Swallows, so dependent
on the aerial insect population for food, leave the north as
progressively colder weather limits the insect numbers. One
of the many long distance travellers in search of warmth and
food is Wilson's Phalarope (*Phalaropus tricolor*), which
occurs in many parts of South America during the southern
spring and summer. At the approach of winter there, it
returns northwards to the United States. These birds depend
on aquatic insect larvae and other small arthropods for food.

In some parts of the world, climatic variations are so
marked that habitats are rich for only a few months of the
year. The animals inhabiting such regions have little choice
but to move. Some mammals follow the pasture to keep up
with the limit of good growth, while fishes appear to follow
the richest currents.

In addition to the food requirements of the adults of a species, there is an obvious need to provide food for the young, and many animal movements are closely linked with the breeding cycle. However, the situation is more complicated than this. There are some birds that move three times a year: for example Swiss Starlings fly to the Netherlands after breeding and then return to Switzerland before going to North Africa, and some ducks move to secluded areas to moult, and then on again to a wintering area. Other birds only move short distances and in some cases, only part of a population migrates.

The problems posed by the migrants are nearly always extremely puzzling. Having established that in lands where winter is colder than summer animals tend to move to follow the food supply, a conflicting situation arises in the tropics. Here seasonal changes are slight and yet some species migrate, at times covering distances of more than 1,000 miles.

Possibly migration is a factor essential for limiting the size of an animal population and maintaining a biological equilibrium. In instances where only some of the population moves, the food supply is more evenly distributed. On the long journey made by Swallows, for example, about fifty per cent

Zebras and many other mammals follow the growth of young grass in spring.

of the birds perish, which is perhaps a natural limitation that prevents depletion of the food supply at each terminus. The famous suicidal movements made by lemmings or Springboks (*Antidorias marsupialis*) can be interpreted in a similar way.

One of the most remarkable facts about migratory behaviour is that it is cyclic, and the movements are not haphazard. The cycles are somehow related to a natural rhythm, which on careful investigation seems to control many aspects of animal behaviour. Inevitably there are animal movements which are exceptional and cannot be considered as true migrations. Frequently the term invasion is used, particularly in cases when an animal is forced out of one habitat into another by an unusual natural phenomenon or by human interference.

Migrant birds. **1** Osprey from northern Europe to southern and tropical Africa. **2** Ruby-throated Hummingbird from tropical America north as far as Labrador. **3** Spine-tailed Swift from China to Japan. **4** Sacred Kingfisher from southern Australia to Malaya, New Guinea and Solomon Islands. **5** Spoon-bill from Europe to Africa.

An upwelling of Antarctic water from the oceanic depths, close to the Peruvian coast, constitutes the cold Humboldt current, which is rich in minerals and plankton, and is the basis of a biological food chain comprising millions of Anchovies (*Engraulis encrasicolus*) and seabirds. Occasionally the current fails, usually around Christmastime, and locally the phenomenon is called the Niño or 'child'. It is caused mainly by an insurgence of warm water from the north, which pushes down from the Gulf of Guayaquil and forces the cold rich water downwards and further out to sea. Two very bad years were 1925 and 1965. As the plankton food supply diminished quickly, the Anchovies moved south and the seabirds were forced to follow. In their millions they entered Chilean waters, but many millions more, weakened by lack of food, died on the Peruvian coast. The beaches were littered with dead and dying birds. After the last Niño some birds returned and the population began to recover, but it will take several years to reach its normal level.

Not only are there natural alterations in the environment, but with new technology, man is able to change the habitats

When the Humboldt Current off the coast of Peru fails periodically many of the seabirds in the region migrate, but others, like these Peruvian Pelicans, starve.

Lake Zabol in Persia is nearly dry now due to an irrigation scheme in neighbouring Afghanistan: people and animals have been forced to move.

and even the climate of large areas of the Earth's surface. Cutting into forests, dam-building, and draining marshes all bring about changes, many of which cannot be reversed. Usually the wildlife is affected. One of the many great projects undertaken in the past few years was the irrigation scheme in south-west Afghanistan. The Helmand River has been dammed and diverted through numerous small canals into surrounding desert. Previously the outflow of this river went into Lake Zabol in south-eastern Iran, and the irrigation scheme has unfortunately resulted in a severe drying of the lake, which has forced much of the avifauna to move north towards the Caspian Sea. What was once a rich life zone is now almost dead. In this particular case the local Iranian tribe of reed-dwellers also moved away as the water level diminished. There are many more examples and, as man occupies more land, such movements, often termed migratory, will become more numerous.

EVOLUTION OF MIGRATORY BEHAVIOUR

It has been suggested that the evolution of migratory behaviour patterns was associated with long-term climatic changes, of which the most obvious was the Great Ice Age. One theory suggested that many non-migratory birds inhabited the entire northern hemisphere during a period when climatic conditions were more constant throughout the year than experienced today. Then as the climate began to change, perhaps as the glaciers moved south, the birds were driven south a little more each year. Furthermore, with each annual retreat of the ice the birds presumably would have moved north again, thus establishing over many generations an innate migratory behaviour pattern. A major flaw in this theory is that most of the species driven south as the Ice Age developed would have been extinct by the time the ice finally retreated.

Maximum extent of the north polar ice during the last glacial stage of the Great Ice Age. The evolution of migration might have been related to the Great Ice Age.

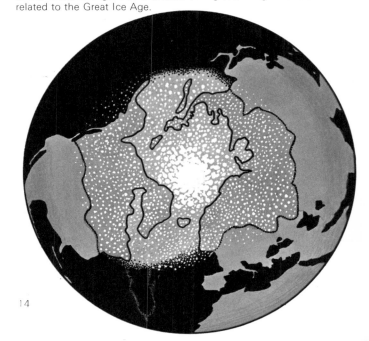

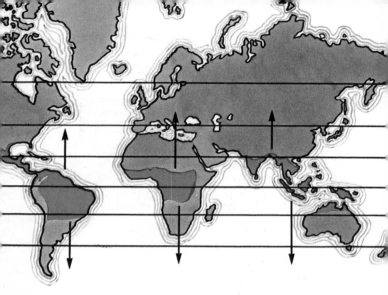

At some time in the past, animals could have spread from the tropical zone (red) into the more temperate areas to the north and south.

Another theory, the Southern Ancestral Home Theory, suggests that the ancestral home of all birds existed within the tropics and that, because of over-population, many species sought new homes to the north where there was less competition for food and nesting sites. Proponents of this theory contend that some individuals of each species went as far north as necessitated by food requirements and with each winter they were forced south again. Certain stimuli could have been important, and the stimulus for reproduction is believed to have sent the birds out of the tropics, while the demand for food could have forced them back to the ancestral home in winter. Again, this theory is not watertight and cannot account for the development of long distance migrations across trackless oceans; nor does it explain how such behaviour became a hereditary characteristic.

These two theories concern the migration of birds, the most mobile of migrants, but the same explanations have been made for the migratory behaviour of other animals.

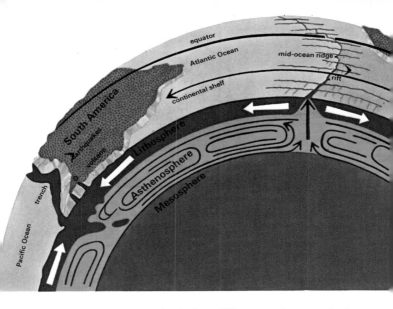

Comparison of rocks and fossils from different continents and other geological evidence indicates that the continents started to drift apart in the Mesozoic era. This movement might have encouraged the development of migratory behaviour.

The fact that pieces of card shaped like the world's continents can be pushed together to make a single unit, that certain rocks of South America match others from West Africa, and that some fossil plants and animals from different continents have been shown to be identical, suggests that the continents were once joined. Recent evidence in fact indicates that the continents started to drift apart about 200 million years ago, and that the drift is continuing possibly at the rate of two or three inches a year.

With a strong case for continental drift having been established, there seems to be an even stronger case for assuming that some migratory behaviour began at the time when the continents were close together. This behaviour then became built into the hereditary mechanism of a species as the continents drew further apart.

Continental drift as the answer to the evolution of migra-

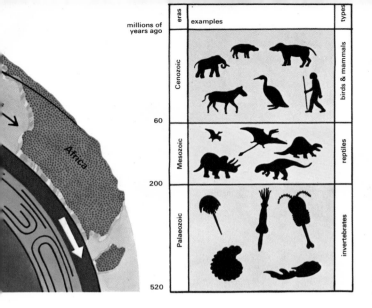

millions of years ago	eras	examples	types
	Cenozoic		birds & mammals
60			
	Mesozoic		reptiles
200			
	Palaeozoic		invertebrates
520			

tory behaviour means accepting the fact that birds either developed their innate homing ability at the time of the drifting, or had possessed it from the earliest stages of their evolution. Furthermore, the theory presupposes that before continental drift began many birds were already making short flights between breeding and feeding areas, and that as the distances increased only individuals with the necessary physiological adaptation survived.

According to this theory, migratory behaviour did not evolve into the present highly developed form because it served a useful purpose, but because it resulted from an inherent behaviour pattern which induced birds to respond to the movement of the continental blocks. Any adaptive features of migration, such as leaving a region at the onset of winter, would consequently be a result of natural selection and not the cause of migration as suggested by the first theories. An objection to this theory is that birds as we know them did not exist at the inception of the drifting, though of course they would have been present before the continents moved very far apart.

WHAT IS MIGRATION?

In searching for a definition of migration, all very slow and one way movements are discarded, as they are not usually considered to be true migrations but are more correctly described as colonizations. However, when looking at the great variety of animal movements it seems convenient to refer to them in general terms as migrations and to subdivide critically after examining each case. Certainly any alteration in the range of a species, including the long flights over water, is important within a review of migrations: some of the journeys are made by mere island-hopping, but others can be compared with the marathons of the true migrants.

In the late 1920s and early 1930s, the Cattle Egret (*Bubulcus ibis*), which until that time was a bird of Africa, southern Europe and Asia, began to expand its territory. Soon afterwards, it had colonized northern South America and extended east to New Guinea. It was not many years before it had

The colonization routes of the Cattle Egret.

spread into the central United States from its foothold in the Guianas and to Australia on the southward march from New Guinea. Now the species is common on the west coast of South America and is moving stage by stage across the desert barrier towards Chile.

The ability of birds to expand or contract their ranges is often shown by unusual evidence. Some of the best comes from fossilized remains, although bird fossils are rare. Discoveries of fossils show that at one time flamingos occurred in Australia and Old World vultures in North America. This indicates that the distribution patterns of species common today are possibly the result of continual evolution in more than one centre, and that there has been colonization followed by further colonization. The precise causes of most dispersals are not clearly defined, but generally the circumstances point to an increase in population demanding a territorial expansion, or a climatic variation leading to a similar movement.

Lemmings on the march and their migration routes in Scandinavia. Red arrows refer to the Arctic lemming, *Dicrostonyx torquatus*, and black ones to the forest lemming, *Myopus schisticolor*.

The famous suicidal marches of the lemmings have fascinated naturalists for years. Although the movements are often referred to as migrations, it seems probable that the population irruptions, which occur every three to five years, over-balance the finely adjusted ecosystem and a suicidal trek is the only answer to over-population.

Each female usually produces four or five young in the breeding season, but periodically the litters are larger and more numerous. This change occurs in seasons when food is abundant, and under these special conditions each female can produce as many as twenty or thirty young. Similar irruptive increases are well known among other animals around the world, although the regulating mechanism is not always as spectacular as the lemming treks.

Normally there is a great increase in the number of predators and thus the equilibrium is re-established. But the lemmings seem to solve the over-crowding problem and subsequent food shortage by making for the sea. At first a few begin to move, then others join them until a flood of these small rodents is rushing headlong for the plains. Nothing stops them: they swim through rivers and ponds,

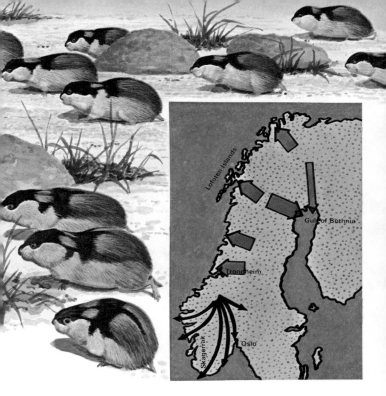

and scramble over buildings and walls until finally they reach the sea. Countless thousands plunge into the water, and while some reach nearby islands, millions die.

Three species of lemming inhabit Scandinavia, occupying forest, tundra and Arctic. Recently in Scandinavia the effect of civilization seems to have altered the balance and mass movements of lemmings are rare.

Lemmings also inhabit the tundra regions of Arctic Canada. Here predators, especially the Canadian Lynx (*Lynx canadensis*), multiply quickly when the lemming population explosions occur, but despite these secondary increases the lemming population gets out of control and only an accidental collective suicide seems to limit the numbers sufficiently to stabilize the food chain.

The Snow Leopard makes a vertical migration on the mountainside.

A definition of migration taken from most dictionaries states that it is movement undertaken by a species periodically from one region or climate to another, for feeding or breeding. This form of definition tends to overlook many unusual movements, especially those made over short distances by lower animal forms, or such dramatic journeys as those of the lemmings.

One recent suggestion is that migration is an adaptation, developed through natural selection, which enables an animal to breed in an area not favourable for its survival at all times of the year. Presupposing that this theory is correct, it could be considered that, as long as the journeys are periodic and are developed by a need for survival, then they can be said to be migratory. Even so, there are some cases which seem close to the limits of a precise definition.

Among mammals, the Snow Leopard (*Uncia uncia*) of central Asia moves on the mountainsides from 18,000 feet in summer down to 6,000 feet in winter. In North America, the Wapiti or North American Deer (*Cervus canadensis*) shows a form of migratory behaviour when it moves down from the mountains with the arrival of winter snows. The deer keep to the same grounds unless the winter is exceptionally severe, and the same ancestral tracks have been used since the movement was first studied. High in the Andes of South America, the rare Taruga or Guemal Deer (*Hippocamelus antisensis*) of Peru makes short seasonal migrations, sometimes over a range of as little as 2,000 feet. Also in Peru, the giant Andean Condor (*Vultur gryphus*) has discovered that in summer there is a rich supply of carrion on the Pacific shore. The bird, the largest of the New World vultures, is a typical inhabitant of the high sierras, though the fortuitous combination of good updraughts and carrion from sea lion nurseries provides an ideal environment at a lower level.

Such migrations are not necessarily habitual, but occur only when the climatic conditions are favourable and they could fall outside the limits of a fine definition.

Andean Condors usually associated with the high mountains, are found on the Pacific coast in summer, taking advantage of the supply of carrion to be found there.

Albatrosses have fascinated many great travellers: they circle the world over the southern oceans, using every nuance of the west winds to carry them on and on, and yet they return unerringly to their nesting grounds, sometimes many years after leaving them. Wandering of this nature is not generally considered to be migration, although certainly the innate ability to orientate in a featureless seascape is a very basic requisite of a migratory bird.

Surprisingly, not all birds are wanderers or even migratory. Some have very restricted ranges and despite their incredible powers of flight do not stray beyond this normal range or even beyond the limits of their individual territory.

One remarkable case of an unusually sedentary bird is that of the Short-eared Owl (*Asio flammeus*), which seems to have settled on Ponape, an idyllic emerald isle of the Caroline group, in Micronesia. The Ponape bird is a sub-species of the Short-eared Owl which occurs widely in Europe and

The Short-eared Owl is well-known for its migratory behaviour, but one sub-species never moves away from the island of Ponape.

Pona
New Guinea

altitude in ft	wing length in mm
115000	120
7000	114-118
3800	108-110
sea level	97-102

Swifts are some of the greatest migrants, but one species in New Guinea has become sedentary. The wing lengths of individuals of this species vary according to the altitude at which they live.

northern Asia, and winters in northern Africa, the Indian sub-continent and China. Far-wandering strays of this species have been recorded in Micronesia, where some probably decided to stay many generations ago. Perhaps if the environmental conditions are right, a species will remain sedentary. Ponape must be just the right habitat for the owl.

Swifts are among the most mobile species of all birds and are some of the greatest migrants, but curiously one swiftlet (*Collocalia esculenta*) in New Guinea has become sedentary. This species occurs at all levels of the mountain slopes and it has been discovered that the wing lengths of the individuals vary according to the altitude of the slope. Such an adaptation confines the swifts of a particular zone to that one level alone. This is an extreme example of a species that has no need to migrate, and that has indeed probably lost the ability to move from a well-defined area.

Wandering and migratory birds are occasionally found in areas far from their normal range. Such strays are probably blown off-course by the wind, or they may drift into a strange region in search of food. Rare visitors attract the attention of naturalists and so detailed records are available from many locations.

European Lapwings (*Vanellus vanellus*) appeared in Newfoundland and eastern Canada in 1927. As they arrived not as solitary strays but in considerable numbers it was assumed

Strays recorded in Britain (above) and in the United States (below).

Strays recorded in Australia.

that a sudden cold spell in Europe had caused a migration, and then the birds had been blown off-course and across the Atlantic by strong winds. Less than a dozen of the species had been recorded in North America before.

In Britain, observations show that more than a hundred species of North American land birds have survived the Atlantic crossing, and among unexpected guests reaching British shores are tiny songbirds, such as kinglets and vireos. In the United States the strays recorded in each area include species from neighbouring regions, as well as strays arriving from Europe, the Arctic and Central America. Some birds often regarded as strays should more correctly be classed as habitually nomadic, as they wander over a wide range of territory in search of food. Of the nomadic species, the cross-bills of North America are famous. They travel from one coniferous forest zone to another, following the erratic seeding of the trees. Their nomadism thus appears to be an adaptation to the local fluctuations in food supply. Animal invasions that are dependent on the abundance of food occur all over the world.

After invasions or drifts, a few individuals may remain behind if the conditions are right and this helps to account for colonization of new territory by a species. Usually, colonizations and invasions are not regarded as true migrations.

Neanderthal sites

others

Spread of early man.

We now know that man and ape have developed from the same early primate stock. The first primates evolved about sixty-five million years ago and proceeded to spread across the world. They made their way to South America by island-hopping, for at that time the southern sub-continent was separated from the north. Early primates spread eastwards through Asia, but did not spread beyond Wallace's Line, which is drawn north of Australasia and New Guinea. Man, as we might recognize him, developed in the Old World and reached the Americas via the Bering Straits route. He then moved south across the Isthmus, and it was relatively only a short time ago, about 10,000 to 15,000 years, that he reached south of Panama. In the later periods of his colonization of the world, man might well have taken to the sea on simple rafts and been carried by ocean currents. Famous for his daring research in this field is Dr Thor Heyerdahl, who has crossed both the Atlantic and Pacific Oceans by raft.

In present times many surviving tribes make annual migrations. One of the most famous is the Persian Bakhtiari.

These people range over the southern deserts, following the pasture: in the winter they move south and in summer they move north, following a route that generations have taken for centuries. Until a few years ago the entire tribe would take days to pass a given spot with their stock and camels, but recently the government has put pressure on such tribes in an attempt to alter their way of life. Soon they may cease to exist.

Far more primitive are some of the South American jungle Indians, particularly the Guayaki in Paraguay, who move through the forest knowing little of the outside world, and so far have not advanced beyond simple hunting. They follow game and insects, taking the same paths in their constant search for food and survival.

Man at this stage of his development shows a need to move with the food supply, and clearly, seasonal changes are an influencing factor. Later aggressive territorial expansion, political forces and other factors begin to override the natural stimuli.

Many tribes surviving to the present day make annual migrations.

Starting from Europe, Scandinavia and the Mediterranean region, man in recent times has made a number of well-documented movements. He has colonized the Americas, much of Africa, Indo-China and Australia, countries where until a few centuries ago there lived only a handful of indigenous people. We tend to refer to the journeys of the settlers as migrations, although obviously most of the movements were in one direction only. The far corners of the world have been colonized by people setting out hopefully to make a better life, or by people searching for gold or a peaceful home.

In the Danube Delta a group of Russians found seclusion among the millions of acres of reed beds. These Lipovenes (the name means 'the men of the lime groves') left southern

Many years ago a group of Russians known as the Lipovenes found seclusion in the wilderness of the Danube Delta.

Today millions of people travel to different parts of the world.

Russia when persecuted by Peter the Great. Today, the Delta is part of Romania, but the Lipovenes continue to live alone and have retained their identity. Their church and folksongs are a reminder of their heritage.

Undoubtedly, man has the desire to acquire new territory, and is beset by the urge to travel. New developments in technology, including jumbo-jets, help him to attain this goal. Although the number of people in the air or on the sea is only a fraction of the world population, the exchange of ideas and cultural contacts possible today could have a significant effect on the future of mankind.

Most of the movements made by man in this age are not truly migratory, but occasionally small groups of workers make annual treks, following seasonal employment. For example, in the southern United States high wages in the harvest season attract many migrant field workers. In Bolivia, the same type of migration is well known, with Indians from the southern provinces moving to the sugar fields of Argentina each year. Other movements of casual labour occur all over the world, and with the activity of the few migrating tribes, this is as near as man gets to a truly migratory status.

INTRODUCTION TO MIGRATORY ANIMALS

Caribou and Reindeer are members of the deer family and are generally considered to be the same species (*Rangifer tarandus*), although found in different parts of the northern hemisphere. They are one of the last remaining large mammals which continue to migrate. In Lapland and Scandinavia, many of the herds are domesticated and the movements are often aided or guided by man. But in Spitzbergen wild Reindeer occur on the grassy plains in summer, and with the approaching autumn the herds move to the seashore to browse on seaweed; then in the winter they move back to the higher ground to forage under the snow for lichens and small plants. Reindeer in Siberia move down from the northern mountains and make for the taiga forests in winter; with the return of spring they move back to higher ground.

The migrations of this species are extremely spectacular.

The Saiga of the Russian steppelands does not migrate along regular paths, unlike the Reindeer, or Caribou, which does.

Saiga

Reindeer

128

gaasper camping amsterdam

NAME:

PLACE NR.:

GAASPER CAMPING AMSTERDAM
LOOSDRECHTDREEF 7, 1108 AZ AMSTERDAM
TEL: 31 (0)20 696 73 26, FAX: 31 (0)20 696 93 69
WWW.GAASPERCAMPING-AMSTERDAM.NL

LYCKLAMA À NIJEHOLT CAMPINGS B.V.

A   11:45   28/07/01

```
        9 ADULT                          72.00
        3 CAMPER                         43.50
        3 ELECTRIC                       13.50
     TOTAL                    HFL 129.00
        CASH              129.00
  8 7179      A    0000-000 11:45    28/07/01
```

Goede reis en tot ziens!
Pleasant journey and so long!
Gute Reise und auf Wiedersehen!
Bon voyage et au revoir!
Bueno vìàje y hasta la vista!
Buono viaggio e arrivederci!

Caribou of North America at one time travelled in herds of nearly 250,000 and as many as 50,000 can still be seen on the march at one time, moving relentlessly at five or six miles an hour. Caribou follow trails made over centuries, and their pattern never changes; the herds leave the higher ground and make for the taiga in winter, to return again northwards for the Arctic summer, when the young are born.

A famous migrant of the Russian steppelands between the Rivers Don and Volga is the Saiga Antelope (*Saiga tatarica*). The distribution of this species has been severely limited by man's depradations and in fact the Soviet government has had to impose restrictions to ensure its survival. Saigas do not follow regular paths because the climate in their arid semi-desert habitat is variable. One severe winter can change their route, and when they face particularly harsh conditions mortality is high. To combat this factor, there are far more females than males. The young are born in traditional calving grounds, and once they can travel, the mothers lead them south.

Reindeer migration routes in northern Europe and Scandinavia.

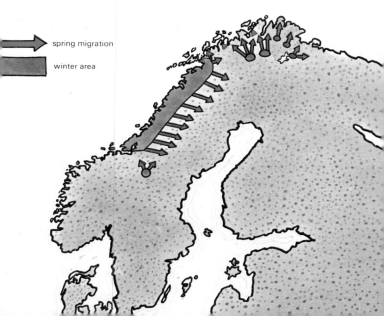

spring migration

winter area

Mass migration of Gnu in Africa.

One of the saddest stories arising from the pioneering days of the United States is the dramatic depletion of the great herds of Bison (*Bison bison*). At one time it was common to see up to four million animals in one herd, and the total population was undoubtedly many millions more. Today, the population is about 12,000 and they survive only because man decided to stop shooting. It was almost too late.

Before the Bison herds were depleted they moved from Texas and New Mexico to Wyoming, South Dakota and Nebraska. The prairies were darkened by the numbers of animals, and the herds took days to pass a given point. They followed the same trails as generations before them, always taking the gentlest gradients and keeping to the contours of the land. The main routes were north to south. Animals wintering in the north of Mexico pushed northwards in the spring and followed the new vegetation on the prairies. After the summer, the herds moved south again. The migrations were not described in detail before the herds were reduced, but it is believed that the herds which spent the winter in Mexico were probably not the same as those found in Canada in the summer. A movement of 300 miles southwards in winter is the generally accepted limit. East-west movements were also known to occur east of the Rockies.

Another example of a much diminished species is the Springbok (*Antidorcas marsupialis*) of South Africa. Conditions for Springboks are no longer the same as when the first observations were made, and their behaviour has changed. At one time they made two distinct types of movement; one was probably truly migratory and regulated by the seasons, the animals following the sprouting vegetation, and the other was the same kind of phenomenon as the lemmings' suicidal march. Many thousands of animals were seen to trek and finally throw themselves into rivers or the sea. The accounts of early settlers suggest that the suicidal treks occurred irregularly every three or four years. These collective sacrifices could have been induced by great competition for food, and with the reduction of the Springboks by man the treks no longer occur.

Springbok and Bison are among the well-known migrant species whose numbers have declined in recent times.

Springbok

Bison

Humpback Whale migrations in the southern seas.

Not all mammals follow the same path year after year, and some species known to make migrations are exceptionally hard to study. Whales pose a problem as they live in a vast environment, but information retrieved from copper darts fired into the blubber has shown that they follow a variety of migratory paths. The Blue Whale (*Sibbaldus musculus*), the Humpback Whale (*Megaptera novaeangliae*) and the Common Rorqual (*Balaenoptera physalus*) are among the species which have provided the most data. It is now known that they tend to move from the Antarctic with the approach of winter. Once the pack ice moves over the rich plankton areas, the whales begin to migrate northwards into the tropical regions, where they give birth to their young, but for each species the pattern is different. The migration patterns of the northern hemisphere species are different again. One species whose movements are well known is the Californian Gray Whale (*Eschrichtius glaucus*). The young are born between November and May in the shallow lagoons of Mexico and California. A few weeks later adults and young travel via the north Pacific Ocean to the Bering Sea, where they encounter an abundance of food. The journey is approximately 6,000 nautical miles, and the distance is covered in about ninety days.

In considering the Arctic seas, the Polar Bear (*Thalarctos maritimus*) must not be forgotten. This animal, which feeds on seals, fishes, seabirds or even some plants during the short summer, seems to lead a nomadic life in its search for food. Their movements are not true migrations, as there are no established routes and no periodicity. Yet they follow the same general direction around the pole, because they move with the drift of pack ice. Occasionally the bears go ahead of the ice, if food is scarce, and it is at such times that they reach the coasts of Scandinavia or Siberia. They return from these forays to rejoin the clockwise-moving currents which take them onwards on their one, endless journey.

Of the seals which are migratory, perhaps the best documented is the Northern or Pribilof Fur Seal (*Callorhinus*

Polar Bear migrations in the Arctic region.

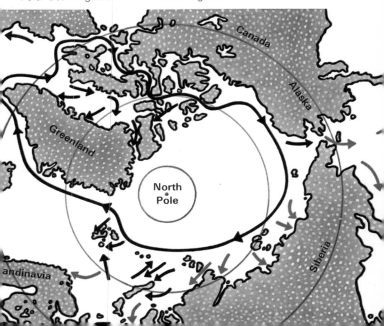

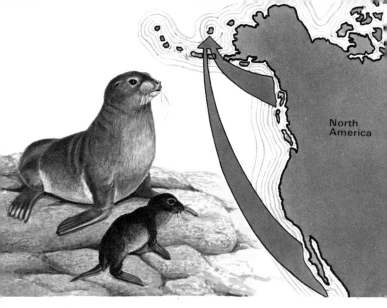

The Pribilof Fur Seal and its migration routes.

ursinus), a species that was seriously depleted by hunters and is now commonly breeding only in the Pribilof Islands. After breeding the females swim about 3,000 miles to the Californian coast, while the males remain in the northern waters near the Aleutian Islands; the sexes meet again on the Pribilofs the following year. Early efforts at marking involved branding, but this was not highly successful, and so a system of tagging evolved in which stainless steel markers are fixed to the hind flipper. Seals can be checked at their breeding beaches and when they reach the most distant point of their migratory route, but it is difficult to make a large number of sightings at points along the route, and so their path can only be assumed to be a straight line between the two termini.

Other seals have been studied, including the Grey or Atlantic Seal (*Halichoerus grypus*) found on British coasts. After breeding, the seals move away to different parts of the sea. By putting a dye on animals at some breeding stations, it has been possible to later identify them. They have been recovered many miles away.

It was generally assumed that with the approach of cold weather, bats searched for a sheltered place and then hibernated. Some, of course, do this, but others make distinct migrations. Occasionally a short journey, of perhaps only forty miles, is undertaken to find a suitable hibernation site. Other migrations are more impressive. A little brown bat (*Myotis* species) of North America hibernates in Vermont, but flies south-east in summer. In Australia, a fruit-eating bat, the Grey-headed Flying Fox (*Pteropus poliocephalus*) migrates from Queensland in October to reach the southern part of the continent in December, and in Europe the Large Mouse-eared Bat (*Myotis myotis*) migrates to the Atlas mountains of North Africa.

Bats may use their echo-location system to help guide them on their migrations. The Grey-headed Flying Fox migrates from northern to southern Australia.

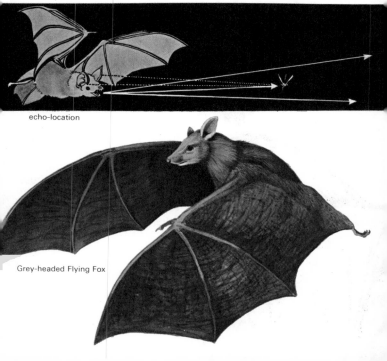

echo-location

Grey-headed Flying Fox

MIGRATION OF BIRDS

Ornithology has a world-wide following, and assistance from dozens of patient observers has meant that much information concerning the movements of birds and related factors, such as the seasons and prevailing weather conditions, has been compiled. Thus some of the most puzzling questions have now been solved, though the precise nature of the mechanism needed for navigation over long distances is still under investigation.

The first step, apart from establishing that birds do indeed move from place to place, is to attempt to define the migratory status of a particular species. Most groupings are determined by the time passed by a species in a territory. Therefore in the north temperate zone four classes of migrants are generally recognized:

Winter visitors Among the birds of this group are those which nest in northern latitudes and move southwards when the Arctic winter

Winter visitors. **1** Bean Goose to Britain. **2** Snow Bunting to Britain. **3** Old Squaw Duck to North America.

freezes over the breeding grounds. Often, such species are widespread on the tundras of northern Europe or America, and they move southwards to relatively smaller areas of marshland, where they winter. The wintering areas frequently support a far greater population in the non-breeding than in the breeding season.

Summer visitors These are the species which nest, not in the extreme north, but in Britain for example, and then move south with the approach of winter. This group includes the familiar Swifts, Swallows, warblers and flycatchers.

Passage migrants This group includes species which pass a short time in a territory, using it as a staging point on the journey from north to south, and again on the return flight. In Britain, the Curlew-Sandpiper (*Calidris ferruginea*) is considered a passage migrant and in the United States, one example is the Solitary Sandpiper (*Tringa solitaria*).

Permanent residents These

Summer visitors. **1** Sanderling to South America. **2** Wood Warbler to U.S.A. **3** Garganey Duck to Britain.

Great Crested Grebe

Blue Jay

Grey Heron

Partial migrants.

are the species which remain throughout the year in one region, although in some instances part of a population migrates, while the other part remains resident.

It is difficult to make a strict ruling for any of the categories, since variations of behaviour exist within a species. Not all the members of a species may leave the wintering ground to return to the breeding ground, and this division is common among those shorebirds which are found on tropical or southern temperate zone beaches. It is unusual for them to breed in the wintering area, but sometimes a few individuals may remain behind and some will breed. European White Storks (*Ciconia ciconia*) have been known to nest in South Africa.

Other variations that occur are the different migration patterns exhibited by closely related species. An example is provided by the Purple Sandpiper (*Calidris maritima*) and Baird's Sandpiper (*C. bairdii*), which both breed in the Arctic of North America, but the former winters in the temperate coastlands of the United States, while the latter is found wintering in the southern temperate zone of South America.

In the southern hemisphere and tropical regions, there are similar categories, although the distances travelled by the migrants are very often much shorter. One contributory factor is the limited temperate region south of the equator, and another factor is the climatic diversity of such continental areas as Australia and South America. Many Australian species are migrants within the continental limits or more strictly some are nomadic as they move to keep pace with the changing habitat. The great variation in latitude from north to south in South America induces a more positive pattern of migration among the southern breeding species. From Tierra del Fuego at the southern tip of the Americas, where winters are hard, some birds move north towards the equator. Particularly spectacular are the migrations of the Ashy-headed Goose (*Chloephaga poliocephala*), which moves from Patagonia to central Argentina and Chile.

Passage migrants.

Solitary Sandpiper in USA

Curlew Sandpiper in Britain

Black Skimmer
in parts of S. America

Cranes, when migrating, fly by day.

Migratory Behaviour of Birds

Migrating birds do not all travel at the same time of day, and some species show distinct preferences; there are many night migrants, some day migrants, and others which migrate by day or night.

Among the day migrants are the cranes. The European Crane (*Megalornis grus*), which is found across much of northern Europe and Scandinavia, is the largest bird of Europe, having a wingspan of six feet. Each spring the arrival of these birds is anticipated with mounting interest across the continent. In the autumn they gather in groups and then commence the journey to Africa. Following well-defined narrow routes, the birds from the western areas move south through France to the north coast of Africa. The birds from Russia move across south-eastern Europe and the Mediterranean to north-eastern Africa and the Nile. Almost to the day, these cranes are seen flying over the same spot year after year.

Birds of prey form another group of daytime migrants. Not all species migrate. Of those that do, many make long journeys; for example Lesser Spotted Eagles (*Aquila pomarina*) nest in south-eastern Europe and depart in late summer for South Africa, and Honey Buzzards (*Pernis apivorus*) leave central Europe for the great tropical forests of the West African Cameroons and Congo.

The Osprey (*Pandion haliaetus*) is widespread throughout the world and is well-known in places such as Scotland, where there are few specimens, or on Long Island, New York, where there are many. Some Ospreys of Europe move south to central and southern Africa in search of open water, which they need since they are dependent on fishes for food. These are caught from the surface by incredibly accurate use of the talons.

The day-migrants group is mainly composed of the larger birds, including those that are independent of the protection offered by darkness. A few small birds are included, the Swift being one example.

Day migrants.

Red-footed Falcon

Red-backed Shrike

American Robin

Typical day and night migrants are geese and many shore-birds. When the geese arrive in Britain from places in the far north, winter is not far away. The birds arrive after a journey from the darkening Arctic, where the midnight sun of summer is replaced by the long gloom of winter. Geese move south from the Arctic lands of Siberia, Russia and Greenland. Greylag Geese (*Anser anser*) fly from their nesting places in southern Russia, Scandinavia and Scotland to points further south. These geese are the most southerly distributed of them all. Others, including the Pink-footed Goose (*A. brachyrhynchus*), or the Bean Goose (*A. fabalis*) arrive from Greenland, Spitzbergen, Scandinavia or Siberia while the White-fronted Goose (*A. albifrons*) moves in from Siberia, Greenland or Russia. In the southern hemisphere the Ashy-headed Goose travels northwards with the onset of winter.

Swans, too, are day or night migrants. In South America, for example, there is the handsome Black-necked Swan (*Cygnus melancoriphus*) which is pure white but for the fine, black, neck plumage. These swans live in the far south,

Some birds make their migratory flight in the evening or during both day and night.

Black-necked Swan

Canada Goose

Great Northern Diver

breeding as far afield as the Falkland Islands. They are power-ful fliers and make short migrations. Occasionally the jour-neys are longer than expected, and some records of Black-necked Swans have been taken on the Juan Fernandez or Robinson Crusoe Islands, which are in the Pacific, 360 miles west of Valparaiso. A stray bird has also been recorded in the unlikely wilderness location of the Atacama desert.

The Whistling Swan (*C. columbianus*) from the far north of North America breeds between Alaska and Hudson Bay, and migrates south-west to California or south-east to Chesapeake Bay and Currituck Sound. A larger North American species is the Trumpeter Swan (*C. buccinator*), which breeds in the western plains from southern Alaska to James Bay, and migrates southward to California and Texas.

Other day or night migrants are the divers and loons. The Great Northern Diver (*Gavia immer*) nests in North America, Iceland, Jan Mayen island and Greenland, and different populations travel to different watering places. From the northern United States they move to the Gulf of Mexico, while the population from Greenland moves to Europe and winters there, from Great Britain to the Mediterranean.

ducks

Night migrants and flight paths of nocturnal spring migrants set free at Champaign, U.S.A., with radio transmitters attached (after Cochran). **V** = Veery, **G** = Grey-cheeked Thrush, **S** = Swainson's Thrush.

In general, the night migrants are small land birds whose migratory behaviour has presumably been adapted to suit their feeding requirements; by flying at night they manage long water crossings, and can feed at each end of each lap of their journey. Additionally, they benefit from the protective cover of darkness.

The migration of the scops owls (*Otus* species) is interesting. They are among the smallest of the owls, and are sometimes called screech owls. The scops or screech owl of Europe (*Otus scops*) is not much larger than a sparrow, and it leaves southern Europe to winter in equatorial Africa.

Coots are nocturnal migrants and the species commonly occurring on European lakes is known to make very long journeys, often covering as much as 450 miles in two days. These birds are not difficult to observe in their habitat, and there are plenty of data on their migrations. However, the

rails and crakes of the same family, the Rallidae, are extremely shy and it is very difficult to determine with certainty their patterns of migration. However, it is known that the Spotted Crake (*Porzana porzana*) nests in an area extending from the Mediterranean to Scandinavia and winters in northern Africa across the continent to the Sudan, while the Corncrake (*Crex crex*) from European marshes reaches as far as the equatorial regions. Both crakes and rails are nocturnal, and their rather strident voices carry across the marshlands adding to the mysterious sounds of the night.

Among the legions of other night migrants are buntings, thrushes and wrens; in fact the majority of small migratory birds. Soon after sunset at migration time they begin their journeys, until the sky is filled with large flocks heading for a new home, sometimes thousands of miles away. When the night fliers are counted, it appears that the greatest numbers are in the air between dusk and a peak at just before midnight; in the early hours of the morning the numbers decline.

49

Extent of Bird Migrations

One of the most remarkable migrants is the small wheatear. There are about twenty species belonging to the thrush family, but instead of inhabiting woodlands and scrub, they have taken to the open country. They are found in many parts of Eurasia, North America and Africa.

The Common Wheatear (*Oenanthe oenanthe*) is an extraordinary migrant. It is found nesting in Europe, the entire breadth of Russia, Greenland and the north of Canada. All the birds, no matter where they are from, spend the winter in Africa. It is a long journey for the European population, but a fantastic marathon for the populations from Canada, as they have to cross the Bering Straits and then the whole of the Soviet Union before turning south. The entire journey represents at least 20,000 miles in a year.

Record-holders of the southern hemisphere include two New Zealand cuckoos, which leave the islands in winter and

Wheatears from Canada cross the Bering Straits and Russia on their journey to Africa.

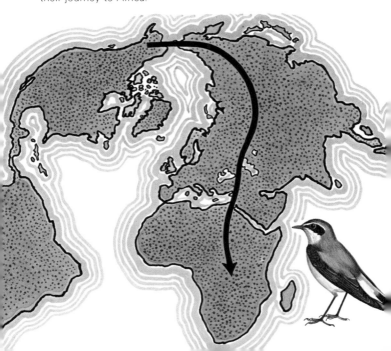

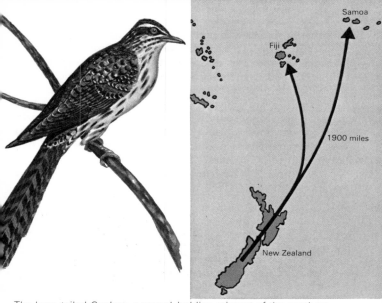

The long-tailed Cuckoo, a record-holding migrant of the southern hemisphere, leaves New Zealand in winter and migrates to Oceania.

move across the sea to Oceania. The fairly mild climate and the insularity of New Zealand suggests that most birds there would be sedentary, and yet these two species show extreme mobility. The Bronze Cuckoo (*Chrysococcyx lucidus*) migrates 2,500 miles, mostly over open sea, to the Solomon Islands, and the Long-tailed Cuckoo (*Urodynamis taitensis*) travels to Fiji and Samoa.

Although these examples are among the most interesting, they are not unique: many species are known to travel thousands of miles on migration. Of the shorebirds, the Siberian Pectoral Sandpiper (*Calidris acuminata*), breeding in Siberia, has been recorded on Tristan da Cunha in the Atlantic, and the Lesser Golden Plover (*Pluvialis dominica*) which nests in northern Canada and Alaska sets off in autumn for the Hawaiian Islands. The journey is more than 2,000 miles over open sea. A few continue the journey to reach Oceania. The Siberian population follows the Asian coastal route southwards to Australia and New Zealand.

Probably the most famous of all long distance migrants is the Arctic Tern (*Sterna paradisaea*). The birds nest in high latitudes around the entire northern hemisphere and in winter they are distributed widely over the Atlantic, Pacific and Indian Oceans. Fairly good information has been collected, from banding experiments, about the routes that they take from the breeding grounds. Some results have been remarkable; for example a bird which had been banded in Russia was recovered in Australia, the distance between the two points being 14,000 miles.

Arctic Terns that nest in Siberia and Alaska fly down the eastern Pacific, while the majority of birds of this species

migration routes ⟶

nesting areas ▬▬▬▬

funnel to the Atlantic and travel down the eastern shores. All the routes take the terns to the Antarctic, where they avoid the winter darkness of the high northern latitudes.

This migration of the Arctic Tern is clearly a post-breeding dispersal which has evolved to enable the birds to follow the food supply, and undoubtedly the routes they take are along the line of the richest ocean currents, or where winds are favourable. Such a migration not only allows large numbers of individuals to be produced in the breeding areas, but it also seems to act as a regulator, limiting the population by the inevitable heavy mortality during the long journey.

The Arctic Tern and its southward migration routes.

Not all bird migrations are as extensive as the long flights of Arctic Terns, and within a sub-continent the size of North America many species make short distance migrations. The usual axis is from north to south away from the cold winter, and into good feeding places. The American cowbirds, grackles and Red-winged Blackbirds (*Agelaius phoeniceus*) nest widely over the northern regions of the continent, and withdraw southwards for the winter. These birds collect in large mixed roosts.

Not all the short distance migrations of birds are on a north to south line. Within a continent, climatic conditions can influence the direction and so can the altitude. In the world's mountainous regions, some species tend to move up or down according to the climate and availability of food. The Lammergeyer or Bearded Vulture (*Gypaëtus barbatus*) feeds on bones left after the other vultures have cleaned a carcass; they are residents of Africa, southern Europe and central Asia. With the approach of winter, the Lammergeyers move down the mountains to avoid the snow.

In North America, the Mountain Quail (*Oreortyx pictus*) of California walks short distances down the mountainsides to avoid the winter snow. The White-capped Water Redstart

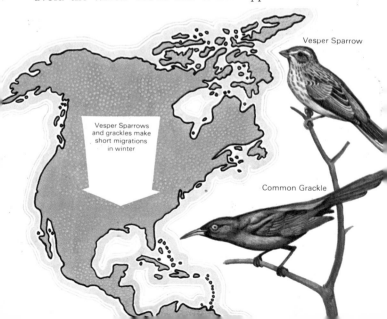

Vesper Sparrow

Vesper Sparrows and grackles make short migrations in winter

Common Grackle

(*Chaimarrornis leucocephalus*) of the Himalayas, found at up to 16,000 feet, descends to the valleys in winter; while in Europe the Wallcreeper (*Tichodroma muraria*) moves down from heights of 12,000 feet. On reflection, it would appear that migrations such as these, where the animal is avoiding wintry conditions, could be substituted by hibernation; and yet it is an extremely rare occurrence among birds. Hummingbirds in cold, high places, such as the Andes, pass the night in a torpor with a great reduction of body temperature, but awaken in the sun of the next day. Only the Colorado Poor-will (*Phalaenoptilus nuttallii*), a nightjar, has so far been recorded as passing the winter in hibernation, and this fact was not discovered until 1946. In autumn, the Poor-wills creep into rock-crevices and their body temperature drops from 102°F to about 65°F. This lowering of their metabolic rate enables them to survive for several months until spring.

Some birds such as the Mountain Quail (1) and the Asian Ibisbill (2) make very short migrations to avoid extremes of temperature. The Poor-will (3) is the only bird known to hibernate.

On a clear night in spring or autumn, if binoculars or a telescope are trained upon the moon, migrants can often be seen in flight.

Methods for Studying Migration

Our knowledge of migrations has come from the results of many different programmes, some of which are extremely sophisticated, while others just involve sheer hard work by groups of ornithologists. In the former class, is the latest attempt to track large, migrating mammals by use of satellites. In early 1970, park wardens in the United States fitted collars holding specially built radio transmitters to a small number of Moose, and these were followed by Nimbus III, orbiting 700 miles above the Earth. By these means, it was possible to determine the position of the animal within limits of one mile. The first experiment was not particularly successful, but it indicated that the system could be developed if funds were available.

Despite such technical advances, older, well-tried methods of migration tracking are still in frequent use. People, such as lighthouse keepers, coastguards, and crew members of weather ships, whose daily life provides the chance to observe migrants, have been enlisted to help in the collection of invaluable data. Lighthouses and television masts, for example, are often in the path of bird migrants, and many nocturnal migrants collide with these obstructions. Each morning, the ground is littered with scores of casualties, and by recording the species, the time and the date, a reasonably accurate assessment can be made of the density of the migratory flocks, and later this information can be related to prevailing weather conditions.

One of the simplest methods used for studying night migrants involves training a telescope on the face of the moon. Birds can be counted as they pass across the field of vision. Furthermore if the migrants can be identified, it is simple to make an approximation of the numbers and the direction of flight. By adding to this information details of wind strength and direction, percentage cloud-cover, temperature and so on, taken from many sources at the same time, a mosaic can be built up, showing the migration routes for a certain day under known conditions.

Night flying migrants are often attracted in thousands to the light from lighthouses or lightships.

Ringing a Black-browed Albatross in the Falkland Islands.

To collect positive information about the movements of a particular bird or group of birds, it is necessary to mark each individual. After the early experiments of marking with coloured cotton ties, the practice of ringing or banding evolved. A light aluminium ring, bearing a serial number and the name of the organization responsible for the work, is clipped around the right leg. The serial numbers are noted before release so that the approximate distance between the places where the bird was ringed and recovered can be determined. The time taken for the journey is not always so clear as recoveries can seldom be made on the day that the bird arrives at its destination. In the scientific world today, information is guarded until the workers are ready to publish their final reports. Since the serial number of the ring is the only clue to the ringing station, only the organization responsible for the project can collate the data.

Often ringing is carried out before the fledglings leave the nest. However, there are certain obvious dangers with this method: for instance the young birds tend to panic, or the parents are suspicious if they see a bright, exotic object in the nest. Despite this, some of the large seabirds are ringed at this time, mainly for ease of capture and also because it provides information from the time that the young leave the nesting ground. One such project is well advanced in the Falkland Islands where a United States research unit has enlisted the aid of local conservationists to band young Black-browed Albatrosses (*Diomedea melanophris*). Some spectacular recoveries have been reported, and a few of the young have returned to the same breeding colonies.

Another method of marking birds, especially effective with those of pale plumage, involves the use of a brightly coloured dye. This system is most useful for those experiments which require short-term observation. If, for example, captive birds are released for the purpose of determining their ability to orientate in strange surroundings, the movements can be followed by an observer in a light aircraft.

Only on occasions when birds can be handled in the nest

Birds dyed bright colours can be followed in aircraft.

The Heligoland Trap (top) is used for capturing small birds while waders, such as flamingos, are caught with a simple snare.

or a dead, banded specimen is collected, is it relatively simple to obtain information. These days, with the number of banded birds reaching into millions, it is necessary to employ methods for capturing large numbers of a particular species.

The techniques vary. Some have not advanced much beyond the system employed by primitive tribes, who use bait and a large net that can be made to fall over the birds when they feed. Better than this is the Heligoland Trap which is a vast funnel of wire mesh, ending in a chamber with a non-return entrance. A trap of this type is best used on fairly open ground where the birds can be driven into the funnel. It is excellent for shorebirds and heathland birds.

Far more spectacular and very effective is the rocket or cannon net method, which is again best used on open ground, heaths and shores. It can also be used with bait or even decoys. A fine net is laid along the ground and folded carefully with one edge secured firmly; along the free edge weights and some explosive devices for propulsion are attached. The net can be fired by remote control from behind a blind when the birds are within range. It is very successful with small birds and hundreds can be caught with one operation.

For wading birds, such as flamingos, which seldom move over firm ground, simple snares can be made and placed across a part of the feeding area; the birds are then gently driven into the prepared area. They have to be collected immediately they have become ensnared to prevent the birds damaging themselves by struggling.

Despite the enormous numbers ringed annually, there is a very low percentage of recoveries, about two per cent for Swallows and 1·1 per cent for finches. The figures are a little better for birds hunted for sport, the percentage for the Greylag Goose being about twenty-four and that for the Teal (*Anas crecca*) sixteen. However, even such small numbers of recoveries can provide sound basic information.

Water birds, such as ducks, can be caught in a cannon net.

From most lines of research there is useful spin-off, and for investigators of migratory behaviour, radar has provided a means of following large groups of bird migrants. When radar was in its infancy during the early part of the Second World War, the operators were often dismayed by unusual patches on their screens. These indications never seemed to coincide with identifiable objects, and so were given the name 'radar angels'. Because the confusion could have led to danger, the angels were investigated, and were found to be the result of reflections from large flocks of birds. Almost immediately the migration specialists moved in, and took advantage of the knowledge by enlisting the cooperation of radar stations. Particularly heavy migrations are seen clearly, and now of course, from the modern radar set it is possible to obtain the height, density and velocity of the flock at distances from five to ten miles. An experienced operator can tell the type of migrant by the height and speed. Generally it is the field observer who makes the vital records of which species are responsible for the angels.

As electronic equipment can be miniaturized to a high degree by using modern components, methods which were used and discarded some years ago are now more efficient and have therefore been re-introduced. Small radio transmitters can now be fitted to the larger birds, and the move-

The image on a radar screen of a flock of birds is diffuse, while that of an aeroplane is more positive (see top left quadrant).

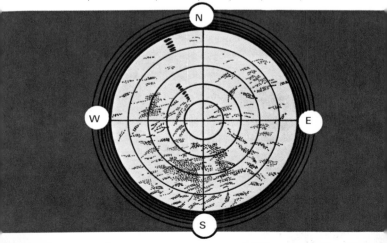

ments are then followed by direction-finding equipment. This method has been used recently for tracing the routes of Andean Condors along the Peruvian coast.

Small electric lights powered by miniature batteries have been attached to ducks and geese, and the birds can be followed visually. The lights are fastened with bands of paper and water-glue so that they fall off when the bird settles on water. If this gear can be miniaturized sufficiently it could have many uses, but it has to be remembered that even the weight of a small aluminium band can be great in comparison with the body weight of a small bird.

The flight paths of Andean Condors have been determined by aligning two, directional aerials with transmitters on the birds.

Swifts feed on the wing.

Altitude of Flight

Radar observations and sightings from aircraft have helped establish the heights at which various species migrate, whereas in the past only reports from mountainous regions had provided the answer to this intriguing question. Obviously, birds have the ability to fly high, but what is the limit of their physical capacity and do they ever reach it? Mountain climbers experience the demand for great physical effort at high altitudes, and they have realized the value of acclimatization before making extremely high climbs. Nevertheless mammals and birds can live at very high altitude. In the Andes some hummingbirds survive close to the snowline at 16,000 feet, while other birds, including the Condor, are seen at over 20,000 feet. Many of the migrants from North America pass along the Pacific coast and thence into the high mountains with apparent ease.

Perhaps the record for high flight comes from the Himalayas, where some geese were seen flying at an estimated altitude of 29,500 feet which must surely indicate that the geese possessed an incredible metabolic rate and were able to adapt easily to a low oxygen pressure.

However, most migrants keep within the range of sea-level to 2,500 feet. A smaller number of species migrate at a height of up to 5,000 feet; about ten per cent at a height of up to 10,000 feet and less than one per cent above that. Geese are among the high fliers, and so are some shorebirds, including sandpipers and plovers. Storks too have been seen at 15,000 feet, while many small songbirds are known to fly at as much as 21,000 feet, although only a few individuals have been recorded at this height. Swallows and Swifts tend to fly at about 5,000 to 6,000 feet, their altitude apparently being limited by the availability of small insects, on which they feed during a migratory flight.

29000 ft — goose

15000 ft — stork

13000 ft — Wilson's Phalarope

2500 ft — plover

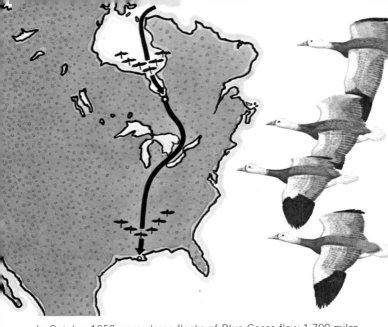

In October 1952, some large flocks of Blue Geese flew 1,700 miles from James Bay to Louisiana in 60 hours.

Velocity of Flight

The flight speed of birds has held the attention of naturalists since the earliest days of banding and recording the journeys of migrants. When the first results of banding experiments were published, some of the average speeds were found to be quite remarkable.

A classic study began by chance in October 1952, when unusually large flocks of Blue Geese (*Anser coerulescens coerulescens*) were seen taking off from near the southern end of James Bay in Canada's Hudson Bay. The next day, pilots of a Canadian airline saw large numbers of the geese in flight at about 6,000 feet just to the north of Lake Huron. A day later the large flocks were seen over southern Illinois at an altitude of about 3,000 feet and on the third day the geese began to arrive at the wintering grounds in Louisiana. Between October 16th and 19th, the birds covered 1,700 miles and almost certainly the flight was accomplished without stopping; the average speed for the distance was nearly thirty miles per hour.

Statistics are available for many other birds. One record flight was made by a Lesser Yellowlegs (*Tringa flavipes*) which flew from New England to the West Indies in six days; the distance is 1,900 miles which is an average of 316 miles per day. Another rapid-flight record is held by a small duck, the Blue-winged Teal (*Anas discors*), which flew from the St Lawrence river to Guyana, a distance of 3,300 miles, in twenty-seven days.

The Arctic Tern has to travel approximately 25,000 miles in nine months. The Cliff Swallow (*Petrochelidon pyrrhonota*), moving northward from California to British Columbia, averages twenty miles a day and then it speeds up to ninety miles a day on nearing its breeding ground in Alaska. Another example is the Grey-cheeked Thrush (*Catharus minimus*), a late migrant, which averages 130 miles per day on its journey from the Gulf of Mexico to Alaska. Again, it increases speed as it approaches the breeding area.

Rate of advance of the Grey-cheeked Thrush on its spring migration northwards through the U.S.A. into Canada.

species	birds tested	distance transported (miles)	% returning	typical speed (miles/day)
Leach's Petrel	61	135-470	67	30
Manx Shearwater	42	265-415	90	200
Laysan Albatross	11	1665-4120	82	100
Gannet	18	213	63	100
Herring Gull	109	214-872	90	60
Common Tern	44	228-404	43	125
Swallow	21	240-310	52	150
Starling	68	200-440	46	25

Table of flight speeds of some migrants.

There are two ways of approaching the question of migration flight speed. Firstly there is the actual flight speed of the bird during the period when it is flying, and then there is the average speed over the entire length of a migratory route. Furthermore, there is usually a difference between the flight speed during migration and the flight speed at times when the bird is not migrating. Generally the speed is greater during migration.

Other factors have to be considered. Winds influence the averages, and the wind speed a hundred feet above the ground can be very different to the ground wind speed. Additionally, in working from averages, discrepancies arise because rest periods may be unwittingly included. Moreover, some of the exceptional speeds attained by birds, such as the 180 miles per hour in steep dives of the Peregrine Falcon (*Falco peregrinus*) are not a true indication of the actual flight speed.

A study of flight speeds was made by Richard Meinertzhagen and although his estimates are among the best available, inevitably they are approximate, as the various influencing factors were not always taken into consideration.

Some of the fastest migrants are the shorebirds, the sandpipers, plovers and others. They move steadily at about forty-five miles per hour. Some of the slowest are the small songbirds which fly at twenty to thirty miles per hour.

The rate of advance across a continent increases as the migrants near the breeding grounds, and the acceleration is fairly constant. In general terms the spring migration is more rapid than the autumn one. An example is given by the Wood Warbler (*Phylloscopus sibilatrix*), which travels from France to Africa in sixty hours but takes only thirty hours on the return journey.

The climate, too, is important, and in North America the spring season advances more quickly in the northern interior and along the west coast than on the Gulf Coast and Mississippi valley. Therefore in spring the rates of advance are seen to vary for species moving along the western and eastern routes.

Mallards (**1**) are among the fastest migrants, usually flying at between 46 and 60 miles per hour. House Sparrows (**2**) are much slower. Peregrine Falcons (**3**) migrate at between 20 and 40 miles per hour, but can attain 180 miles per hour in dives.

Patterns of Bird Migration

If certain isolated exceptions are put aside it can be assumed that the main migration routes of birds are along the north-south axis. As winter approaches in the northern hemisphere, the migrants move south towards the equator and some species even fly on into the southern hemisphere, reaching into southern Africa and South America.

As well as the major lines of direction, some strong east-west components are involved, particularly in the Old World region, where the Himalayan mountain ranges act as a barrier and deflect many migrants westward. We see that the wheatears move across Asia to Africa, only turning south when past the mountainous regions.

Another cause of deflection is the existence of warm ocean currents, such as the Gulf Stream which creates a warmer zone on a land mass, thereby attracting migrants from colder interior regions. Even the shape of a continent can cause migrants to follow distinct routes, and in North America,

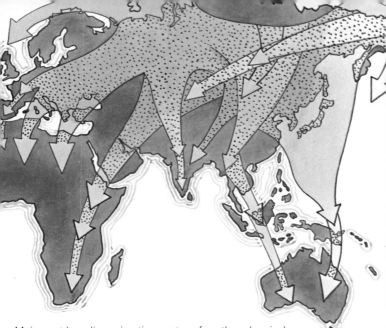

Main post breeding migration routes of northern hemisphere breeding birds, showing the extent of their penetration south of the equator.

birds are funnelled towards Central America and the Isthmus of Panama and from there into South America by their tendency to follow the land rather than cross the sea.

On a map, some deflections are seen as diagonal movements across the north-south axis. Among the many species which do not follow the simple route are the Western Sandpipers (*Calidris mauri*) of North America; they breed in Alaska and cross the sub-continent to winter in Florida.

Common Eider Ducks (*Somateria mollissima*), also migrants, fly 1,000 miles westward from the Canadian Arctic before turning south through the Bering Straits to winter in the Bering Sea area. Another feature of certain flight patterns, notably among waterbirds such as ducks and grebes, is that they migrate to the nearest coastline and then continue along the coast, southwards in the case of post-breeding northern hemisphere migrations.

The pattern is not very different in the southern hemisphere, with the main axis again being north-south. The main difference is that there is little penetration of the northern hemisphere by migrants from the south.

As the winter approaches the southernmost regions of South America, some birds move north into the centre of the sub-continent where the cold is less intense, or even to the equatorial regions. The Slender-billed Plover (*Pluvianellus socialis*) nests in the extreme south in Patagonia or Tierra del Fuego, and in June and July it is found in central and northern Chile, as well as similar latitudes of Argentina. Sometimes a few reach as far as Ecuador. One very tiny migrant from the south is a hummingbird – the Green-backed Firecrown (*Sephanoides sephanoides*) – of which a few pairs nest as far south as Tierra del Fuego. This bird, though a migrant, has been observed in a torpid state in very cold weather, but it is not certain whether it remains in this condition for very long periods.

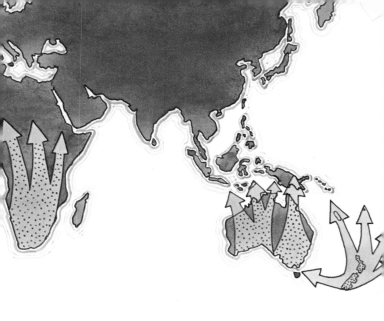

Main post-breeding migration routes of some southern hemisphere land birds, indicating the lightness of penetration north of the equator.

On the other side of the world, the patterns of migration in Australia, New Zealand and New Guinea are complicated by the proximity of the land masses and there are many birds which move across the intervening sea north to New Guinea, or diagonally from New Zealand to Australia. Within the continental island mass of Australia there is a north-south migratory movement which follows the climatic changes during the year. One of the species moving far afield is the Sacred Kingfisher (*Halcyon sancta*) which leaves the southern regions of Australia in March and flies northwards to Malaya, New Guinea and the Solomon Islands.

The African migration patterns are controlled far more by rainfall and humidity, rather like the inter-tropical regions of South America and Asia, and the movements tend to cover short distances and be complicated by numerous local factors.

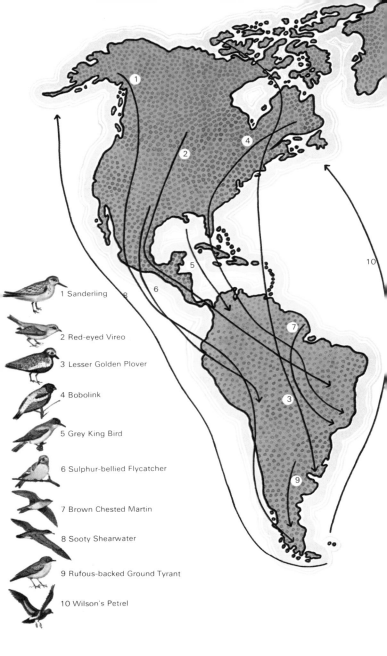

1 Sanderling

2 Red-eyed Vireo

3 Lesser Golden Plover

4 Bobolink

5 Grey King Bird

6 Sulphur-bellied Flycatcher

7 Brown Chested Martin

8 Sooty Shearwater

9 Rufous-backed Ground Tyrant

10 Wilson's Petrel

The Americas, spanning the entire distance from the Arctic to within a few degrees of the Antarctic circle, present the longest possible north-south journey overland. Major routes on the journey north to south are termed 'flyways'. The two coastal routes are distinct; then there are the east and west routes, as well as a central route and Mississippi route in the United States. In south America, the flyways extend either down the Andes or on either side of the chain or along the coasts.

Some shorebirds, such as the plovers and sandpipers, are noteworthy for their great journeys from the far north to the far south. Summer visitors to Chile include the Semi-palmated Plover (*Charadrius semipalmatus*), the Black-bellied Plover (*Pluvialis squatarola*) and, occasionally, the Lesser Golden Plover; all of which breed in Arctic regions. The Lesser Golden Plover is the best known and is a more regular visitor to Argentina. The pre-nuptial (spring) and post-breeding (autumn) migrations of this species follow different courses. On the southward journey, the birds travel east to Nova Scotia and then over the ocean to South America. For the return, the course is to the west, and the route is across the Isthmus and Gulf of Mexico, then up the Mississippi valley to the breeding grounds. The young birds follow the second route in both directions.

The icterid Bobolink (*Dolichonyx oryzivorous*) is a great migrant. It breeds across southern Canada and the northern United States and travels across the Gulf of Mexico and the Caribbean to winter in Argentina, Brazil and Bolivia.

A remarkable example of oceanic migration is the flight of Wilson's Petrel (*Oceanites oceanicus*). These birds nest on the islands around Cape Horn and in Antarctica and after breeding spread north-eastwards across the Atlantic reaching Africa and Newfoundland. They congregate in the North Atlantic in July, move across to Europe and then southwards again for the summer nesting season. Wilson's Petrel takes advantage of the wind currents and in fact moves with the wind but follows a pattern that ensures a safe return to one of the world's most tempestuous regions.

Map of post-breeding routes between North and South America.

When land birds are faced with a major water crossing as in the Caribbean, Australasia and Mediterranean regions, distinct preferences for the crossing point are apparent.

Of the birds that fly across the Mediterranean between Europe and Africa, the large day migrants with a gliding type of flight are the ones which avoid the wide stretches of open water. Storks head for one end of the Mediterranean or the other, to cross at the narrowest points by the Strait of Gibraltar or via the Bosphorus and Gulf of Suez. Sometimes they are seen in thousands at the crossing points or along their favoured flyways, such as the Jordan valley or the Gulf of Suez. On the way south the European White Stork population divides into two branches and thousands of birds funnel through the crossing points before spreading out again in Africa. Almost twice as many birds take the eastern route and some reach as far as South Africa. Those crossing

Flight paths across the Mediterranean. Purple arrows indicate routes followed by birds which avoid crossing the open sea and red arrows denote routes favoured by most bird migrants.

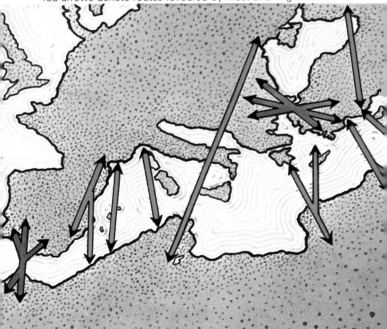

White Stork

Honey Buzzard

Short-toed Eagle

Some migrant birds of the Mediterranean region.

at Gibraltar cross the western Sahara and reach the central regions of Africa.

Although birds of prey use the same crossing points, most of the smaller birds take a variety of routes across the sea. Once again, they obviously prefer to take the shortest possible way and cross between the major islands to minimize the time spent over water. Unfortunately these migrants are mainly nocturnal, and so they have not been studied in detail. However, we do know that whether they brave the open sea crossing or choose the narrowest points, many of the migrants are then faced by the Sahara, and not all of them complete the journey. Some species cross in a single step which usually takes them about sixty hours; others descend to an oasis for rest before continuing. Of course, the most favoured route is along the Nile valley into the north-eastern region of Africa, and it is the Ethiopian zone which receives the greatest proportion of European migrants.

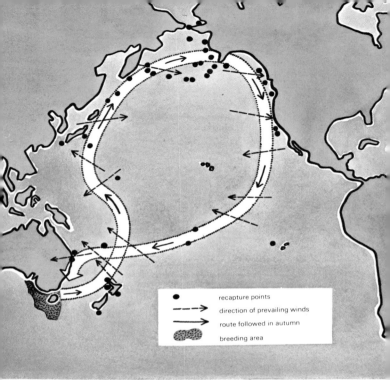

●	recapture points
---▶	direction of prevailing winds
——▶	route followed in autumn
⬤⬤	breeding area

Migration of the Short-tailed Shearwater.

The crossing of the Mediterranean seems an extraordinary feat for small birds, but some of the most amazing journeys over open sea are those of migrants travelling along the Pacific routes. The two New Zealand cuckoos and some Arctic-nesting birds make particularly outstanding journeys. The Bristle-thighed Curlew (*Numenius tahitiensis*) reaches Polynesia from Alaska, and the Bar-tailed Godwit (*Limosa lapponica*), a visitor to Australia, also comes from Alaska.

However, one of the most astonishing flights is made by the small, Short-tailed (Slender-billed) Shearwater or Tasmanian Mutton Bird (*Puffinus tenuirostris*), which makes a great, loop migration which eventually takes it back to its breeding ground in the southern regions of Australia. The course once more is dictated by the prevailing winds and food supply. This is a migratory pattern characteristic of the pelagic seabirds. These are the birds that move far away from the coasts, as opposed to the group including gulls, which tends to stay near the coasts. The most migratory of the gulls is the Lesser Black-backed Gull (*Larus fuscus*), a partial migrant which moves from the Baltic as far south as Africa.

Penguins are familiar and amusing inhabitants of the southern oceans, nesting either in Antarctica or the lands fringing the south, where the coasts are bathed by cold currents. These birds are exceptionally powerful swimmers, having specially adapted, flipper-like wings. As they swim they appear to move in short bursts, curving out of the water, then diving in again, and thrusting forward quickly. Often penguin migrations involve journeys across both ice and open sea. Adults and juveniles move northward in autumn and return again in the summer. On the Falkland Islands, the Magellan Penguin (*Spheniscus magellanicus*), which possesses a weird jackass-like call, is especially vociferous in the autumn. One local naturalist humourously interpreted the wailing as 'We're going, going away', for within a week or two of the start of the persistent calling the last of the Magellans has gone, northwards to the warmer water off the coast of northern Argentina.

Some migrant birds of the Pacific region.

Bristle-thighed Curlew

Short-tailed Shearwater

Lesser Golden Plover

The Hawk Mountain Sanctuary, U.S.A.

We tend to think of migrations in terms of a large number of individuals making their journey at the same time and in large groups rather than singly. Indeed, it is strange that many birds which are normally solitary are found in flocks of thousands on migration, and this even extends in some places to the birds of prey, which are strongly territorial. Particularly large congregations of migrants are found in the flyways along favoured routes, especially where they have to negotiate an obstacle. Obvious gathering points are narrow straits or the narrow cols in mountain ranges where migrants can avoid flying high.

In the United States a famous place for observing migrations is the Hawk Mountain Sanctuary; many thousands of migrants, including large numbers of birds of prey, fly past each day. Another excellent observation point is the Portachuelo Pass in the Venezuelan lesser Andes. It is well-known for the immense flocks of migrating insects, especially butterflies, and birds, which pass through it. It is no more than a shallow depression in the coastal range, but it opens the way to the vast interior.

For migrants which are normally solitary, the rest places or stop-over points along the route are places where they can be seen in large groups. There are marshlands along British estuaries for shorebirds, and reed beds throughout Europe which are favoured by migratory Swallows.

In Europe, the Danube Delta with many thousands of acres of reed beds and open pools is especially good, and not far away is the Nile Delta region, or the Carmargue in France. On the other side of the world, the Salamanca Island at the mouth of the River Magdalena in Colombia is a little known but exceedingly rich zone which has been established as a national reserve.

Despite the unusual congregation of normally solitary individuals of a species in these stop-over places, the groups of different species do not appear to intermingle on the ground but keep to distinct areas, which is a great help to anyone collecting data.

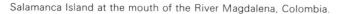
Salamanca Island at the mouth of the River Magdalena, Colombia.

When some of the first associations were made between radar angels and migrating birds, the culprits were identified as huge numbers of Starlings (*Sturnus vulgaris*). These highly gregarious birds gather in immense groups, as any Londoner

The movement of different groups of Starlings from different parts of Britain to western Europe, Scandinavia and Russia.

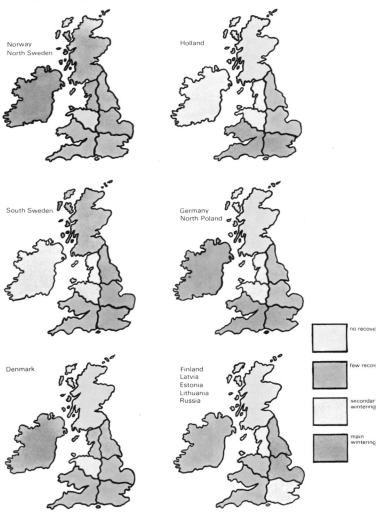

Norway
North Sweden

Holland

South Sweden

Germany
North Poland

Denmark

Finland
Latvia
Estonia
Lithuania
Russia

no recove

few reco

secondar
wintering

main
wintering

Starlings gathering in London.

will testify. All the Starlings from the suburbs move into central London in the evening, travelling along a corridor about five miles wide until they reach their roosts, usually the major buildings. Of Old World origin, the Starling, thanks to help from man, now has an almost world-wide distribution; South America is the only continent where it has not gained a foothold.

Starlings are typical partial migrants; those which occur in Britain and western Europe are erratic in their movements, while those from further north and east are far more migratory. One of the most interesting features of the migrations is that the flocks are independent of each other, and do not usually mix. These different populations have been shown to have different winter ranges which are determined by the place of origin. There is plenty of information concerning the movements of Starlings in Europe, and some reports indicate the extent of the numbers involved. One observation made in the month of November from a lightship off eastern England was that 1,000 birds per hour were passing by on their way from Europe at the onset of a cold winter.

Sometimes huge flocks of juvenile Starlings are seen over the countryside. Instead of undertaking a true migration they disperse in all directions from the nesting area, which avoids the formation of heavy concentrations around the nesting site. Post-breeding dispersal of this type does not have the same characteristics as a migration, within the limits of the definition, as the motivation is entirely different and there is no periodic two-way movement.

Swallows on migration.

Swallows probably are the most famous of all migrants and in the first days of ornithology some naturalists believed that these birds hibernated. Not until men travelled the world and migrants were recorded was it clear that swallows from Europe made the journey to Africa and back each year. There are more than eighty species of swallow and they are scattered widely and evenly throughout the world. The ordinary Swallow (*Hirundo rustica*) of Europe, Asia and North America is sometimes called the Barn Swallow and is the species most familiar in Britain.

Very often swallows and swifts are confused, but they are distinctly different groups and have different migratory habits. Swifts arrive and leave the northern latitudes with unvarying regularity and winter in southern Africa. The Barn Swallows, on the other hand, do not all move at the same time and the southward movement extends from August to October. Also, while swifts spend much of their life in the air, and at night seem to fly higher, swallows come to the ground to roost in 'dormitories', such as large reed beds.

The northward movement of the swallow is governed largely by the weather and there is a close relationship between the front of the migration and the 48°F isotherm. As the temperature increases in the north the swallows keep pace,

Main migration routes of swallows.

although occasionally one or two individuals arrive before the main flocks and succumb to the last cold days before spring.

Hundreds of thousands of swallows have been banded, well over a quarter of a million of these in Britain alone. It has been discovered that depending on their country of origin, the European swallows make for a different part of Africa when they fly south. The North American Barn Swallow winters in South America, the Asiatic populations move southwards to Malaya and the Philippines. A close relative of the Barn Swallow is the Welcome Swallow

(*Hirundo tahitica neoxena*) of Australia, which moves northward towards the equator during winter.

To single out any group of birds for special discussion is difficult; however, ducks and geese present some of the most exciting arrival and departure scenes of the year. Parts of central and southern Europe are the wintering grounds for many species which breed in the Arctic.

Ducks have a rather specialized migratory behaviour which is influenced by their moult. Most birds usually lose their feathers one by one over a period of time that is sufficient to allow the first ones to grow again, so that the animal is not incapacitated or made defenceless. Ducks are different. After nesting they lose all their long wing feathers – the primaries – and so become incapable of flight. They have become adapted to making two migrations, which enable them to survive. The first takes place between the mating season and the autumn, when they make a moult migration to a place of concealment, usually marshes or swamps where they can moult undis-

Three sub-species of the Bean Goose winter in Europe, and though their wintering areas are localized, they tend to wander over the whole of the region. One sub-species, shown by the stippled area. is more restricted and has little contact with the other two.

turbed. The second is the main migration to their wintering grounds.

There is another unusual feature of duck migrations which is apparent when the birds return to the nesting grounds. Unlike most migrants which tend to return to the same area (if not the same place) to nest, ducks have no well-defined home. On occasions a bird found in Britain one year is seen in Europe or Scandinavia the next, and it is impossible to predict the movement of an individual. This change of nesting area has been attributed to the fact that birds from a number of different populations mix together in the wintering area, which could result in one or other partner leading the mate to a strange nesting area, or a duck simply being led along a different route after joining ducks from another region.

Not all ducks are migratory. The steamer ducks of southern South America are flightless and thus tend to remain in one place and some of the southern stiff-tailed ducks (Oxyurini) do not migrate either. Of these, the Australian Musk Duck (*Biziura lobata*) was at one time thought to be flightless. In fact, it can fly, but does so mainly at night and often walks between swamps.

Observers in a blind at a wildlife sanctuary.

Homing

One of the most fascinating aspects of any migration is the ability of the birds to orientate and return to their nesting grounds. Homing is often accomplished with phenomenal accuracy, and although many feasible suggestions have been made to explain the mechanism of this behaviour, the matter seems as much of a mystery as ever.

Experiments with Manx Shearwaters (*Puffinus puffinus*) have demonstrated this homing ability in a most spectacular fashion. In one experiment two of these small pelagic seabirds were taken from their nesting burrows on Skokholm, an island off the Welsh coast, and were transported to Venice some 900 miles away in a straight line, although more than 3,700 miles away by the sea route. After fourteen days one of the birds had returned to the nest, having taken the sea route. This meant that it had covered 265 miles per day. Another incredible return was made by Shearwater number AX6587 which had been taken to Boston, Massachusetts, and released. It was back at its Skokholm nest in twelve and a half days, which is an average of 244 miles per day for the 3,050 mile journey.

Later this trans-Atlantic experiment was reversed when

Manx Shearwaters and their nesting holes on the Island of Skokholm off the Pembrokeshire coast, Wales.

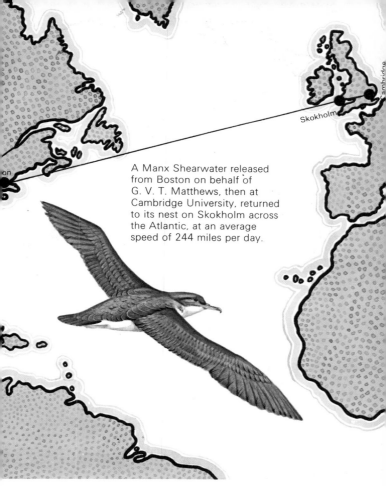

A Manx Shearwater released from Boston on behalf of G. V. T. Matthews, then at Cambridge University, returned to its nest on Skokholm across the Atlantic, at an average speed of 244 miles per day.

seven Leach's Petrels (*Oceanodroma leucorhoa*), taken from an island off the coast of Maine, United States, were released from the Sussex coast of Britain. The first two birds were back in Maine in less than two weeks.

Of the several categories into which homing behaviour can be divided, the form exhibited by the Manx Shearwaters shows the highest degree of orientation. In this case the birds were released in a distant territory unknown to them, and

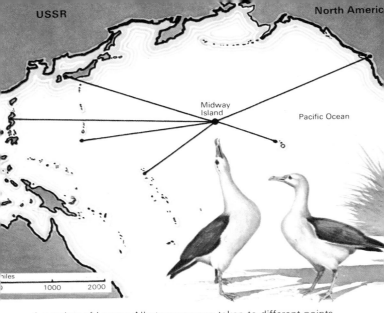

Midway
Island

Pacific Ocean

miles

| 1000 | 2000 |

A number of Laysan Albatrosses were taken to different points fringing the Pacific and 14 birds returned to Midway Island at speeds ranging from 128 to 317 miles per day.

far from the normal migration routes; the distances involved and the speed at which they were covered completely eliminates any possibility of homing by chance.

The same kind of homing ability was demonstrated by a famous experiment using eighteen Laysan Albatrosses (*Diomedea immutabilis*) from Midway Island. Each albatross was removed from an active nest and taken to a point on the edge of the Pacific. Altogether fourteen of the eighteen returned and their speeds ranged from 128 to 317 miles per day. Their flights number among the longest successful homing flights ever made.

In the Antarctic an investigation was made to discover whether Adelie Penguins (*Pygoscelis adeliae*) possess a high degree of orientation ability. These birds live in the pack-ice region all the time except in the breeding season. At the beginning of the Antarctic spring they begin their shoreward migration. They gather in huge colonies, which in some places number as many as half a million individuals, and each bird displays what is termed a 'site tenacity', returning not only to the same colony but invariably to the same nest. Some of the experimental work proved that even when ice covered the nest site, the birds could find their own old nest, which was no more than a simple collection of pebbles revealed as the ice melted.

There are obvious differences between birds involved in homing experiments and birds making a normal migration. Firstly, the true migrants are affected by a group influence, as all the individuals of one species tend to move in the same direction, and secondly many of the homing experiments have been carried out on nesting birds, or with pigeons which have been bred for racing. Furthermore, some of the most successful homing experiments with displaced wild birds have been made with the pelagic seabirds. However, despite the apparent conflicts which can be read into the results of experiments, it is probable that the homing birds and true migrants have similar methods of navigation and these can be used effectively both on migration or when homing birds are displaced.

Adelie Penguins in the Antarctic manage to return to their nest site each year with a high degree of accuracy, so displaying very good orientation.

Much of the experimental work of bird orientation research has been conducted with homing pigeons.

In searching for an answer to the orientation problem, much of the experimental work has been conducted with homing pigeons. As a sport, pigeon racing began in Belgium in about 1825. Before that time pigeons had been used for message carrying by ancient Greeks, Romans and Egyptians. In the Pacific, frigate birds have been used for inter-island communication, and some attempts to use Swallows for message carrying were made in Europe.

In the last 150 years, the racing pigeon has been subjected to very selective breeding, and so the stock has been greatly improved and the sport now commands a large following. From the experimental point of view an important fact is often overlooked – there is a wide range of homing ability among racing pigeons, and only five to ten per cent can make accurate, high speed returns. The training of racing pigeons has been turned into a fine art. There is an emphasis on separating the male from the female until after the successful flight; the homing is also improved when the birds are feeding or incubating and good results have come from establishing a close association with food and the loft. Nevertheless, data from pigeon homing experiments have helped with defining three main types of homing. Dr D. R. Griffin of Harvard University pioneered this work.

Type I relates to when the birds are released in a familiar area and orientate by known landmarks, and when released in unfamiliar territory wander about looking for landmarks that they might recognize.

Type II relates to when the birds are set free, and fly off in a definite direction, sometimes, although not always, in the direction that they have been trained to take. Once they have decided on a direction they hold to it, but so far the reasons behind the decision making are not understood.

Type III is the kind of homing demonstrated by the Laysan Albatrosses of Midway. When a bird is released in unfamiliar territory it makes a decisive move very quickly and returns unerringly to the nest.

Frigate birds have been used by some Pacific Islanders for message carrying.

Orientation

As well as employing training methods to heighten the affinity of a pigeon for its home, the birds can be trained to recognize landmarks. The birds are released at greater and greater distances from the loft, so that they recognize much of the surrounding territory. This kind of ability, which is a form of memory training, is believed to be possessed by many wild birds. Large soaring birds such as vultures, eagles, storks and seabirds of the coastal regions, spend hours covering many miles around their home and evidently can recognize the main features of the land surface. Mountains, buildings and coastlines are particularly important signposts.

In order to discover whether a pigeon can remember the landmarks near the loft, one experimenter trained pigeons to

Birds home to known landmarks when they are near enough to spot them. Pigeons can see their loft or an eagle can recognize a rocky crag.

pigeons

Golden Eagle

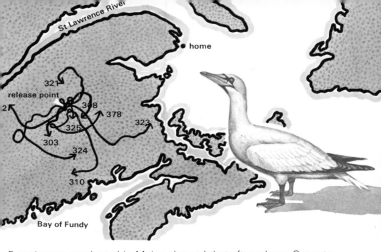

Experiments conducted in Maine showed that after release Gannets explored in spirals until they recognized the territory.

peck at a feature on an aerial photograph, and by a system of rewards, the pattern became established and the pigeon repeated the pecking as much as four years later. Another positive result came after fixing a large, bright indicator on a pole above a loft: returns from releases nearby improved considerably.

There is a pitfall, however, in the suggestion that homing to known landmarks is the main basis for orientation, as other experiments have proved. If pigeons are released a very long way from their territory, it is most unusual for any to return, and those which do manage to find their way back make wide-ranging exploratory flights. Once they find a familiar feature they return quickly to the loft.

Some of the classic experiments on exploratory behaviour were made by Dr Griffin. He released Gannets (*Sula bassana*) in unfamiliar surroundings and then observations of their flight pattern were made from a light aircraft. Although two-thirds of the birds did find their way back and were obviously using known landmarks in the final stages of the flight, in general, the Gannets made many long meandering flights, which showed that they did not possess the same orientation faculties as long-distance migrants.

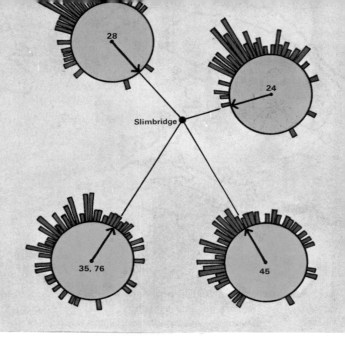

Experimenting with Mallards at Slimbridge, G. V. T. Matthews noted that the birds flew north-west from the point of release. This inexplicable behaviour was termed 'nonsense orientation'.

One of the most curious tendencies shown by some birds when released is what has been called 'nonsense orientation'. This term was created by Dr G. V. T. Matthews, who performed a series of experiments with Mallards (*Anas platyrhynchos*) which came from a largely non-migratory population from south-west England. Regardless of sex, age, previous experience, distance or direction from home, wind direction, whether it was day or night, and so on, the Mallard always flew north-west from the point of release. The direction was not maintained for more than twenty minutes, by which time most of the ducks had landed or departed from the original direction. Other groups that came from London parks and Sweden showed an initial orientation to the south-east. Nonsense orientation has also been discovered in other birds.

A possible reason for this behaviour is that it is innate, and that it helps birds to re-locate themselves if they are blown off-course; in this way it could be associated with Type I orientation. But before examining this hypothesis more carefully, it is worthwhile to note that the homing ability so perfectly shown by pigeons is also seen in a number of wild land birds, as well as the pelagic seabirds, and that the ability to home accurately is clearly greatest in species with a strong migratory behaviour. Conversely, small land birds with a limited feeding territory seldom manage to return if displaced even a few miles. It would thus appear that there is a strong case for genetically inherited behaviour patterns being important factors. Even more experiments have been made to investigate this.

Homing performances of many birds have been tested. Of a group of Herring Gulls transported 214–872 miles, 90% returned at an average speed of 60 miles a day; 43% of a group of Common Terns transported 228–404 miles averaged 125 miles per day; and 46% of a group of Starlings transported 200–440 miles averaged 25 miles per day.

Herring Gull

Common Tern

Starling

One of the most obvious indications of inherited migratory behaviour is shown by the habits of some juvenile birds. The adult Cuckoo leaves its young to the care of another bird and eventually the juvenile makes the same migration as the adult, without having been able to learn the route from its parents. Similarly, young and adult Lesser Golden Plovers take different routes on the post-breeding migration, and yet all of them arrive in Argentina.

In searching for further evidence, biologists have held back young birds in the breeding area until the adults have departed, or reared young in areas where the species does not breed. Generally results have shown that the delayed and unnaturally reared birds follow the normal migration direction.

To eliminate the possibility that the experimental birds joined overflying normal migrants, 271 Hooded Crows (*Corvus corone cornix*) were caught on spring migration in Germany and set free 630 miles to the south-west, at a point where the migration had ceased. The result was not conclusive but the general direction of the movement was to the north-east, the normal migration direction.

From this sort of evidence it has been assumed that the young bird is innately equipped for a flight of a certain bearing and distance to an area that is unknown to it. It also appears that the route followed by birds displaced on migration remains roughly parallel to the normal route and there is little or no angular correction shown by young birds. They

Young Cuckoos (1) make the same migration as the adults, but start at a later date. Young Lesser Golden Plovers (2) migrate to the same area as the adults, but follow a different route.

end up in the breeding area in the same latitude as, but to one side of, the main population. However, displaced adults adjust their course.

When migrating Hooded Crows were moved 630 miles south-west from Rossiten to Frankfurt, where the local migration had ceased, the normal north-eastern movement was still strongly favoured.

Navigation

If there were a shift of a fraction of a degree in the flight direction of the Bristle-thighed Curlews, the birds would miss Tahiti by hundreds of miles. Somehow these birds and other migrants must be able to navigate. How do they do it?

Some early theories were based on the supposition that birds could detect the gradients in certain geophysical forces. By responding to the variations of stimulus strength and relating these to an innate or learned pattern, a bird could move along a predetermined path. Particularly attractive in the list of known forces was the Earth's magnetic field. One idea suggested that the bird might be a form of conductor which, moving through the magnetic field, would be creating a small difference in potential between the two ends of the conductor (the bird), and if this could be measured by some sensory cells, then by some very complicated 'calculations', the animal could determine its position. However, as a flying potentiometer, a bird would need to be able to measure within one millionth of a volt, and this is unlikely. To check this and other theories involving the earth's magnetic field, birds were equipped with tiny magnets to upset their sensitivity: their navigational ability was found to remain unaffected.

In some experiments magnets are attached to birds so that their sensitivity to the Earth's magnetic field is upset.

magnet

pigeon

Even more remote is the intriguing possibility of birds' possessing a sensitivity to Corioli's Force, which is produced by the effect of the rotation of the Earth, and a change of velocity of an object moving relative to the Earth's surface. The force can be interpreted as a sideways force upon the bird, when the change of velocity is explained by the bird flying at constant speed northwards across the Earth's sphere, thereby getting closer to the axis. One theory suggests that a bird can detect this sideways force, but this would require that the bird's speed would have to be maintained within 0·2 miles per hour and its weight held constant within one or two grams – even then it would have to detect a force of less than 1/6000 that of gravity.

More hopeful would seem to be the effect of Corioli's Force on the fluid of the inner ear, which is responsible for the perception of acceleration. However, the fluid is permanently in a state of molecular agitation, known as Brownian movement, which can be shown mathematically to be strong enough to mask any effect Corioli's Force might have.

Inner ear of a bird, and grid of Corioli's Force (black lines) and equal magnetic vertical force over part of North America.

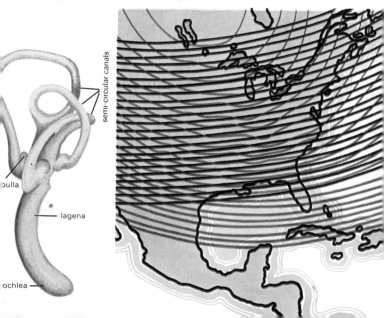

semi-circular canals

bulla

lagena

cochlea

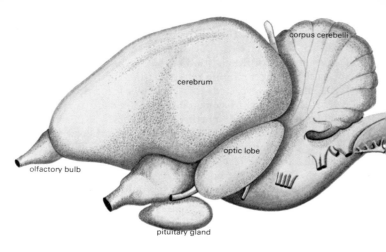

olfactory bulb

cerebrum

corpus cerebelli

optic lobe

pituitary gland

Before continuing with the more feasible theories of navigation, some other features of migratory behaviour need consideration. What kind of stimulus sets the migrants off on their journey and what external factors can influence the migrations?

Certain atmospheric conditions are closely related to migrations – temperature, rainfall and food supply can hardly be separated. High winds and cloud cover also upset migrants and it has been shown that when pigeons are released on an overcast day, they often fail to return to the loft. So it would seem reasonable to suppose that the changing skies of autumn and spring might act as a stimulus for the start of a migration. Also, somewhere behind the scenes, the breeding cycle of the birds is active, and a cyclic, glandular activity has to be taken into account.

The control of the sex glands is largely the work of the anterior part of the pituitary gland, situated in the lower part of the brain. The pituitary has been found to respond to light intensity, and can therefore be considered as the go-between which coordinates the external and internal influencing factors. Hormones or 'chemical triggers' are produced in the body by a system of endocrine glands, of which the pituitary has been likened to the conductor of an orchestra. Of the hormones produced by the pituitary, one

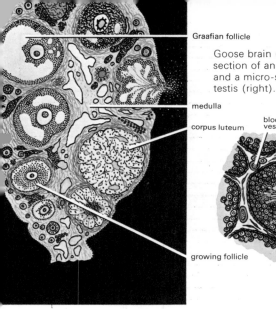

Graafian follicle

Goose brain (left), a thin
section of an ovary (centre)
and a micro-section of a
testis (right).

medulla

corpus luteum

growing follicle

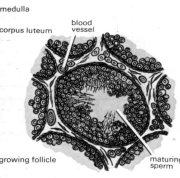

blood vessel

maturing sperm

stimulates the follicles of the ovary, another activates the growth of cells in the testes and yet another works on the thyroid gland, which in turn controls the storage of fat.

The effect of day length is regarded as a major external influence which brings about changes which eventually stimulate the bird to migrate. In one experiment light was directed through the thin skull of ducks on to the pituitary area. After this treatment hormones were secreted. Other research followed the course of artificially shortening the day length, and birds subjected to this were found to be slowly returning to the pre-spring breeding condition. It was postulated that the increasing length of daylight hours in spring must cause an acceleration in the development of the breeding condition.

Other factors include hormonal activity controlling the deposition of fat, and the increase in the metabolic rate, both of which occur before the start of migration. 'Migratory restlessness', observed in songbirds held captive in cages, probably heralds the migration, and external and internal factors seem closely related at this stage.

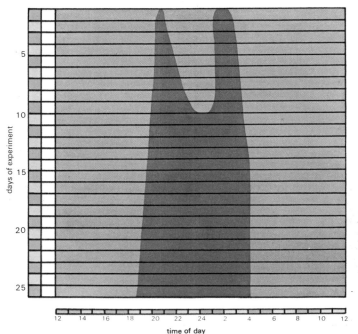

The activity record of flying squirrels kept in darkness for 26 days indicates that a biological clock maintains to a high degree the daily activity pattern.

As well as the hormonal and external factors which clearly seem to influence the timing of migration, there are suspicions that there could be an even deeper and more firmly established timing mechanism.

The general name 'biological clock' is given to the internal rhythms that an animal is now known to possess, and research indicates that there may be more than one of these mechanisms, and that they probably occur within the chemistry of individual living cells. One of the reasons for believing that the 'clock' exists at the cellular level, is that very precise rhythms have even been found in simple, unicellular animals.

An idea of the precision with which such clocks seem to

work is given by the egg-laying habits of the Short-tailed Shearwater. These birds nest in south-eastern Australia, and on one island eighty-five per cent of the birds lay their single egg within three days of the peak dates which, according to historical records, have been the 25th and 26th of November for over a century. One must not forget that these shearwaters migrate across the Pacific to the Aleutians, and back again, thereby passing through a wide variation of temperature and day length. Furthermore, experiments with captive shearwaters indicate that the gonads develop at the same rate as those of the birds on migration. Good evidence for precise internal rhythms also comes from birds living in the tropics, where there is hardly any seasonal variation to act upon them externally. Sooty Terns (*Sterna fuscata*) which nest on Ascension Island have a reproductive cycle which is completed in less than a year, in exactly 280 days, in fact.

Most of the early studies of biological clocks were made on activity cycles, and in one case some flying squirrels were kept in constant darkness for twenty-six days. There was little variation in the pattern of their daily activity. Often the rhythms are called *circadian* – derived from *circa* (about) and *dies* (day) – as the cycles do not always last exactly twenty-four hours. If the clock cycle diverges from a twenty-four-hour one by even a few minutes it will drift out of phase with sun time, and an accurate twenty-four-hour rhythm is essential if some of the most advanced theories of navigation are to be acceptable.

A population of Short-tailed Shearwaters has laid its eggs within 3 days of certain peak dates for over a century.

Biological clocks are now suspected of playing an important part in stimulating migration, and many studies have involved artificial shifts of the timing. This kind of experiment has indicated that there can be a close and necessary link between the clock and a particular function of the brain.

The Indigo Bunting (*Passerina cyanea*) is a familiar migrant in the eastern United States. It moves south to Mexico, Central America and the Caribbean region in the autumn. In attempting to discover the means by which they navigate, S. T. Emlen put some in a planetarium where, as nocturnal migrants, he expected them to be affected by the stars, but surprisingly the birds appeared to ignore the artificial heavens. At the time it was spring outside and the birds always tried to head north. The next step was to expose the birds to periods of daylight which lengthened faster than the natural advance into summer. By this method, Emlen

Working with Indigo Buntings in the U.S.A., S. T. Emlen discovered that the internal biological clock determines the time of migration, although the birds react to seasonal changes of the stars, especially the Polaris star.

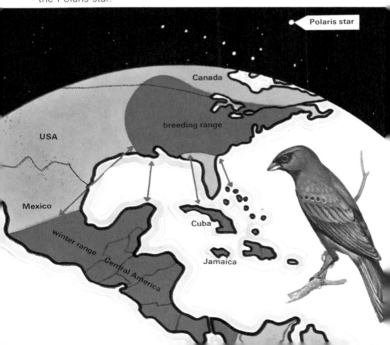

Changing star patterns can be produced in a dark, domed room with sophisticated optical instruments. This is the principle of the planetarium, used in experiments with nocturnal migrants.

was able to advance their biological clocks by six months, and although it was only spring outside, the Indigo Buntings showed physiological changes associated with the autumnal southward migration. When exposed to the spring star patterns in the planetarium they seemed determined to fly south instead of to the north as they should have done in springtime. Emlen concluded that their biological clock was responsible for the response and change of direction. To complete the story, all the stars were removed and under these conditions the birds were completely confused; but after replacing the Polaris star, which is visible all the year in the northern hemisphere, the birds regained their sense of direction.

Emlen's and other people's discoveries point to some form of navigation which demands a celestial point of reference, and a biological clock which controls the choice of direction according to the seasons.

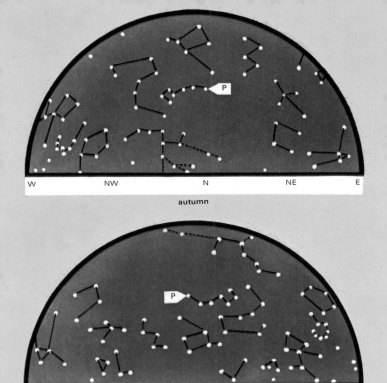

autumn

spring

Further research has revealed that some nocturnal migrants can apparently remember a direction which they took up before sunset, and this direction is held during their flights. Even more curiously, Garden Warblers (*Sylvia borin*) and Blackcaps (*S. atricapilla*) are known to navigate without having previously seen the sun. Dr F. Sauer exposed hand-reared birds in a special cage. These birds had never seen the natural sky, and yet after a period of confusion they took up the normal direction favoured by the local population. It was also noticed that the warblers would move around the cage and take up the correct alignment before they flew off.

By using a rotating perch, it was possible to move the birds and then watch them take up the correct direction again, but on cloudy nights this experiment failed to work, the birds appearing to be confused, although if there was a break in the cloud and a few constellations were visible, the birds re-aligned themselves.

Sauer's experiments were among the first in this field. He continued them by placing Whitethroats (*S. communis*) inside the planetarium: they responded normally to the artificial stars. To verify this he rotated the star pattern through 180 degrees, and the birds followed, which seemed conclusive proof that stars are a vital signpost to night migrants. Acceptance of this presupposes that birds such as Whitethroats and Indigo Buntings must be able to recognize constellations or the Polaris star, and that they have a biological clock by which they can determine the correct time. Also, when they see a night sky they must know the direction they have to follow.

For this type of direction location, birds must possess acute vision and the brain, head, and eye are adapted accordingly, although it could be said that good sight is in any case essential for feeding and watchfulness. However, one anatomical feature remains a mystery: within the eyeball is a small structure known as the pecten and this would appear to impair rather than enhance the vision. It is possible that the pecten is a form of artificial horizon or even a device to help the bird align itself with the stars but so far its use is not fully understood.

In the avian eye a blood-filled wedge, the pecten, occupies a place which could otherwise be filled with sensitive cells and so it produces a blind spot. Its use is not fully understood.

Man can, of course, navigate by the sun and stars, but several calculations are involved. A point defined on the Earth's surface is given an exact latitude and longitude, and the apparent movement of the sun is not the same in the southern and northern hemispheres; however, in the northern hemisphere between the North Pole and latitudes 23° to 54°, the sun appears to move from east to west and is passing to the south; in the southern hemisphere the opposite situation occurs. To determine latitude, the observer takes the angle between sun and horizon at midday, which if the date is known will lead to the answer. By taking the azimuth, or the relation of the sun to north by a vertical line to the horizon, the longitude can be determined, but this requires knowing the time at Greenwich.

If a bird on migration uses the sun, it would need to make

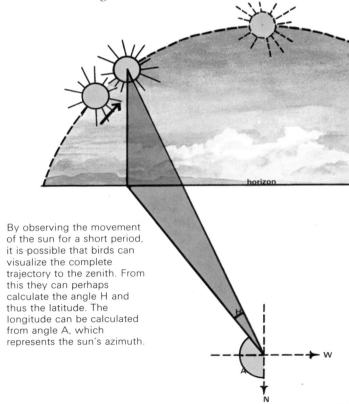

By observing the movement of the sun for a short period, it is possible that birds can visualize the complete trajectory to the zenith. From this they can perhaps calculate the angle H and thus the latitude. The longitude can be calculated from angle A, which represents the sun's azimuth.

such calculations and compensations in order to maintain the correct flight path, and obviously it cannot apply the reasoning used by man. Yet from a number of experiments enough evidence has been accumulated to demonstrate that birds can orientate by the sun.

The most famous tests were made by Gustav Kramer who put Starlings in a specially constructed, round cage. The cage had a uniform interior so that there could be no reference point; then six windows were placed equidistant around the enclosure. Outside each of these windows a vane and a mirror were fixed so that, by moving them, the apparent direction of the sun could be altered. When all the windows were opened and the mirrors were not used, the sun was seen in its normal position by the birds. This was carried out at the time of the spring migration, and they

Sailors use the sextant to plot their position.

orientated to the north-west and showed migratory restlessness. When the direction of the sun's rays was altered, the birds changed their direction accordingly. This system provided an infinite variety of experiments. Kramer found that the birds were confused in diffuse light; he saw them react when they were influenced by a reflection of sky close to the sun. By placing an artificial magnetic field in the vicinity with no effect on the Starlings, he concluded that the magnetic field of the Earth was not involved.

From the positive results of further experimental work with Starlings it can be assumed that birds can take the movement of the sun into account when orientating. This is almost certainly due to their internal biological clock.

Having established these facts there remains only the need of an adequate theory to explain how the bird manages to make this system of navigation work at its own level. G. V. T. Matthews has put forward one solution which suggests that by relatively short observations of the sun, a bird

G. Kramer's experiments with Starlings in a cage revealed that they need the direction of sunlight to orientate. 1 The light was uninterrupted. 2 and 3 Mirrors deflected the sun's rays and the birds orientated in a different position.

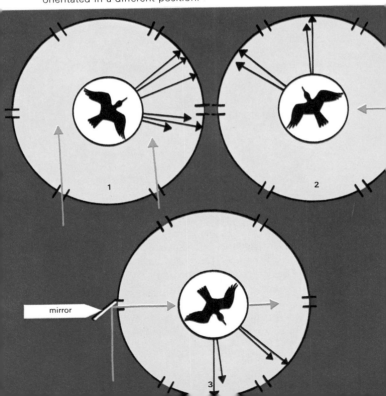

mirror

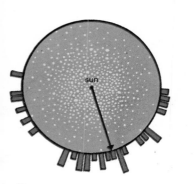
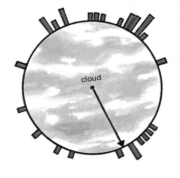

Pigeons released in cloudy weather became disorientated. Purple lines indicate the direction of flight and the arrow points homewards.

can deduce the rest of the arc which the sun will traverse during the day. While making this observation, the bird must also deduce its longitudinal position by measuring the time displacement between the position of the sun and the position the sun would be in if seen from the birds' destination. Obviously, this kind of theory requires the bird to be able to extrapolate the sun's entire trajectory, and remember one point on its migratory arc. Such abilities might seem to be beyond the range of accuracy of the avian senses, but there would seem good reason to believe that the migrants can assess information received from their perceptors, and that the process is rapid and intuitive.

Other theories also involve navigation by the sun, and some of these suggest a far lower degree of sophistication in the coordination of the senses. Perhaps no more is necessary than for a bird to observe the sun's altitude at a given moment and compare it with a memorized altitude of the sun at home at the same time. The migrant would not follow a straight course by this method, but make the journey in a series of curves, before finally homing to known landmarks.

Inevitably all theories have critics. Despite suggestions that birds can be influenced by radiations from unknown sources or perhaps cosmic rays, the fact that when pigeons are released in cloudy conditions they scatter and many fail to return home seems to provide fairly conclusive proof for a form of celestial navigation.

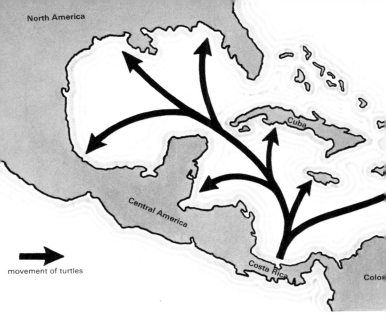

North America

Cuba

Central America

Costa Rica

Colom

movement of turtles

Turtle movements in the Caribbean.

MIGRATION OF REPTILES AND AMPHIBIANS

The story of the marine turtle is a sad one. Not only are they traditional inhabitants of some of the world's warmest oceans, but they are high on the list of the world's delicacies. Perhaps it is not strictly true to say that the turtle soup trade is destroying them, but certainly protein demands of some poorer communities are ensuring that the turtle is on the list of endangered species.

It has been known for a long time that turtles migrate. From the Brazilian coast, Green Turtles (*Chelonia mydas*) migrate about 2,000 miles to Ascension Island in mid-Atlantic. After nesting they return to Brazil. This is possibly the longest migration of any reptile. Kemp's Loggerhead (*Lepidochelys kempi*) occurs from the Caribbean to Cape Cod, and has also been caught in the Mediterranean and off European coasts. This species makes an annual migration to the Gulf of Mexico where it lays its eggs on beaches in the

Tampico district.

Most of the recent studies of sea turtles and their migrations have been made by Dr Archie Carr. He has carried out extensive tagging programmes and has followed marked turtles from aircraft and boats. He has even fitted miniature radio transmitters to the shells in order to trace the animals' movements. The beaches of Costa Rica provided a base and a good supply of turtles. The results of his studies showed that after egg laying there was a wide dispersal in the Caribbean region. Another very interesting feature came to light from the experiments: turtles hatched on a particular beach seemed to return to almost the same beach area. These animals therefore must possess the ability to navigate, and in their case there is the additional complication that they are in a marine environment. The turtles may derive some benefit from the knowledge recently acquired by man of their return migration to the home beach, since conservationists can plan protection of a specific area of coastline.

Turtles are now marked with metal tags attached to the shell.

Occasionally in the Caribbean area, vast numbers of turtles appear on the beach at the same time and the phenomenon is well known to fishermen and poachers who take their toll. This kind of behaviour has not been fully studied, but it seems likely that it is associated with particular weather conditions. Turtles leave the sea at night to move up the beach, and usually they prefer a clear sky and the hours before midnight; the timing allows them long enough to lay their eggs and return to the water before dawn.

Reptiles are usually shy and solitary, and only gregarious during the breeding season. Few make migrations of the classic form shown by birds: other than turtles only certain sea snakes show a distinct migratory pattern. Sea snakes are related to the cobras, and are all highly venomous. The longest reach over eight feet, but most are smaller, not much more than three feet long. They are typically found in coastal regions of the warmer oceans. The bodies of many species of sea snakes are laterally flattened, this being an adaptation to swimming, for greater propulsion is provided during the side to side motion of the body. Most species breed at sea, although of the sea snakes which migrate some breed ashore. When on land they move by using large, ventral scales. The eggs are laid in rocky places where there are caves and crevices.

Most frogs and toads make some form of annual migration

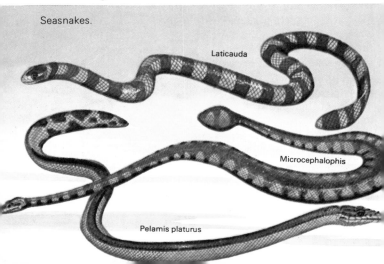

Seasnakes.

Laticauda

Microcephalophis

Pelamis platurus

Even after a pond has been filled in, frogs and toads tend to return to the spot in the breeding season.

to breed. Like reptiles, the amphibians are normally solitary and are distributed over a large area. In the breeding period they congregate in certain places which are used year after year and chosen in preference to any other site. Sometimes when a new estate is built, small ponds are drained or streams have to be diverted, and even when the area has become totally dry, the frogs will return to the spot where they gathered in previous years. The method of navigation has been studied and some species are known to use celestial signposts. In at least one case, frogs were found to orientate under day and night conditions, but not at times when the sky was cloudy.

MIGRATION OF FISHES

The oceans, which cover some seven tenths of the world's surface, and the huge rivers and lakes provide a very special environment. Within this watery habitat, fishes have adapted to suit most of the existing conditions. Some are famous migrants like the eel or salmon and there are others which move from place to place in response to stimuli which are only conjecture at present. For a fish, there are several choices of direction; obviously they can move up or down, and from cold water to warm, but then there are also variations in salinity, and richer currents where the food supply is good. Fish migration is thus a complicated subject even before considering the problem of navigation.

An initial classification of the types of migrant yields three main categories. There are species which breed in fresh water and move to the sea for feeding: these are termed anadromous and an example is the salmon. Then there are species which breed in the sea and move to freshwater habitats for feeding: these are termed catadromous fishes and the eel provides an example. Finally there are those

In response to the stimuli of current, temperature and concentration of food fishes move in many directions.

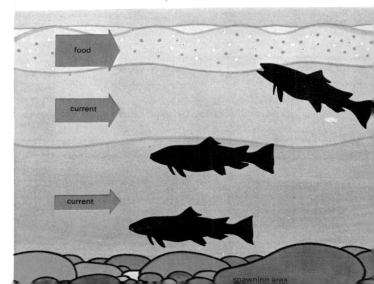

food

current

current

spawning area

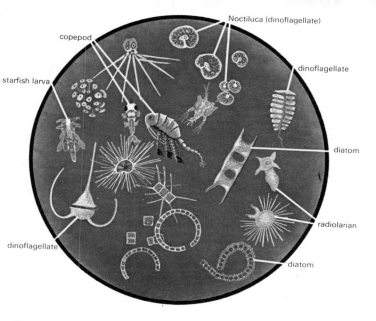

Noctiluca (dinoflagellate)

copepod

dinoflagellate

starfish larva

diatom

dinoflagellate

radiolarian

diatom

The minute animals and plants living in surface waters and collectively known as plankton form a rich food source for many fishes.

species which live permanently either in salt water or fresh water and conduct their migrations within their particular environment. In the first two categories, the fishes make journeys which can truly be classified as migrations, but some of the other movements made by fishes in one permanent environment are not necessarily truly migratory. Of this third group, the Mackerel (*Scomber scombrus*) is an example, and here some confusion is bound to occur. In summer the Mackerel move in close to the English Channel coasts, and can be caught in the shallow bays; then as winter cools the coastal waters they move into deeper water, where the temperature is stabilized. The coastal waters in the north cool first and so the Mackerel seem to be moving on a north to south migration, but in fact they are leaving the coastal waters progressively from north to south, in advance of the approaching winter.

The master of a trawler knows from experience where he is likely to make a good catch and this know-how is hard-earned from many hours on the bridge, watching as the trawl is taken in. At times the nets are bulging and at others they are mysteriously empty. Trawlermen keep in touch with other vessels by radio and they hear reports of fish movements over a wide area. Thus fishing becomes a job for highly practical men who can make the best of any information and even relate it to known migrations.

In the North Sea region, Cod migration has been studied, and there is a distinction between the North Sea population and those of the Barents Sea and Spitzbergen area, which in turn are separate from the population around Iceland. For spawning the Cod (*Gadus morhua*) move into the shallow areas during February, March and April and names like Dogger Bank, Ling Bank, and Fisher Bank are famous in fishing circles, as these are places where the trawlers congregate at the best times of the year.

Already migration patterns are fairly clear for important species in the great fishing areas, but the job is far more difficult than working with birds and mammals, for, as well as the problem of the sea itself, the migrations are often

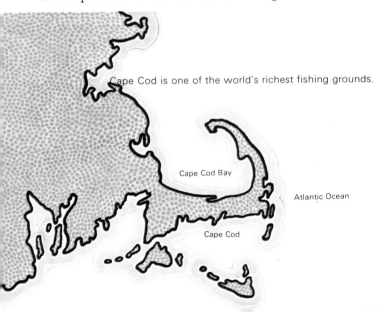

Cape Cod is one of the world's richest fishing grounds.

Cape Cod Bay

Atlantic Ocean

Cape Cod

complex. There is the difficulty of following fishes for long distances, particularly when the shoals move into deep-water zones. One place that has received a lot of attention is the shallow water region around Cape Cod. It is one of the richest fishing grounds in the world. The shore waters are occupied by warm-water fishes in summer and cold-water fishes in winter. Bottom fishes, such as flounders and sea robins, move offshore into warmer, deeper water as the shore water temperature falls in autumn, but at present it is not known whether or not they move south. The Menhaden (*Brevoortia tyrannus*) arrive in spring and leave again in autumn: this is another movement associated with temperature and the species is abundant along the southern coast at any season due to the influence of the Gulf Stream. Other species enter the region as the water cools; Cod arrive from the north-east in late autumn and when it is colder still Long-horned Sculpin (*Myoxocephalus octodecemspinosus*) are abundant.

Some of the fishes found in the Cape Cod region.

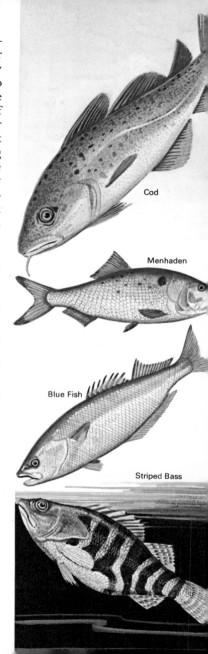

Cod

Menhaden

Blue Fish

Striped Bass

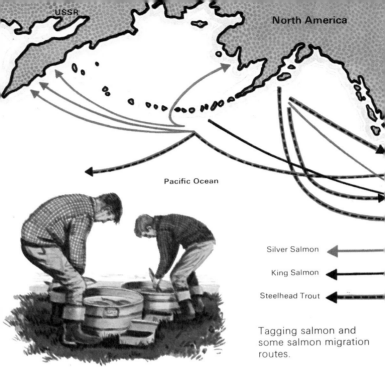

USSR
North America

Pacific Ocean

Silver Salmon
King Salmon
Steelhead Trout

Tagging salmon and
some salmon migration
routes.

The life histories of salmon are known in detail. There are
seven species, including the Atlantic Salmon (*Salmo salar*) of
European coasts and rivers, and several species of Pacific
salmon which occur along the coasts of America and Asia.
Differences exist between cycles of individual species, but
the basic principles are similar. The Pacific salmon returns
from the sea to the rivers in November and December; they
seek out spawning grounds, with gravel bottoms and fast-
flowing water, in the headwaters. The female makes a trench
about two feet long and deposits the eggs, which are then
fertilized by the male. They hatch in the spring.

At an early stage the larvae are extremely tiny, transparent
and heavily endowed with a yolk sac, containing nourishment
for their development. Later the young fry are able to feed on
small insects and crustaceans, and they grow until by the end
of the summer they are about two or three inches long. The

young salmon remain in the fresh water for some time. They then descend the rivers to the sea as smolts. At this point there is some variation between the species. The young of the Pacific Pink Salmon (*Oncorhynchus gorbuscha*) move to the sea soon after hatching, while at the other extreme, the young of the Atlantic Salmon stay in fresh water until the seventh year.

The smolts stop for a short while in the estuary before moving into the sea, after which the migration becomes difficult to follow. However, it is known that once in the ocean they disperse in many directions. In the course of tagging experiments one fish was recorded 3,000 miles from its home river. Methods for identifying salmon now include physiological and immunological tests which can be made on the basis that different populations of salmon rarely mix, and so it is possible to distinguish salmon of specific rivers. The key to this approach is that salmon return to the river where they were hatched. Often there is a four year intervening period between the time they leave and the return, but somehow they manage to locate their own river or stream, and amazingly, they find their way upriver to the exact stream where they hatched. If a wrong turning is taken the fish quickly retraces its path to find the correct one.

Salmon returning to spawning areas negotiate many barriers.

European Eels (*Anguilla anguilla*) spawn in the Sargasso Sea in the Atlantic, east of the Caribbean, and larvae, the leptocephali, rise to the surface at the beginning of summer and feed on the plankton. They measure only about five millimetres, are leaf-like, transparent and quite unlike the adults. Their movements are determined by the ocean currents; those which manage to stay with the Gulf Stream are carried across the Atlantic, but any which are swept north into colder regions perish.

When the leptocephali reach the shores of Europe they change into smaller, white replicas of the adult eels and are termed elvers. They enter estuaries and commence the ascent of the rivers.

Their movement upstream can be accounted for by the fact that elvers are known to react to the current and always head into it, moving only from salt to fresh water. The ability to detect slight differences in the salinity of the water is possibly an important factor in the navigation mechanism of fishes.

The larval and adult stages of an eel.

Migration routes of European Eels.

After eight to fourteen years, adult eels descend the rivers, usually moving on dark nights or in flood conditions, and head for the sea. Suspiciously, very few adults have been caught at sea between Europe and the Sargasso, and there is some doubt about the movements of eels once they are back in the ocean. An interesting theory has been put forward by Dr D. W. Tucker who points out that evidence for the return trip is sparse. He contends that the few eels caught in the North Sea do not seem strong enough to make a long journey across the Atlantic and also that as no eels have been caught in the Strait of Gibraltar it is possible that there is only one eel breeding in the Sargasso – the American species (*A. rostrata*). Any larvae of this eel carried by the Gulf Stream to Europe would develop under different conditions, which would account for the different number of vertebrae in each species (the American Eel has fewer than the European). Experimental evidence shows that if larvae of a particular species are hatched and grown under different temperature conditions, those in the warmest water have fewer vertebrae.

Ocean currents and the presence of plankton can be related to what appear to be migrations of many fishes. The food chain commences with phytoplankton, found in places where there is an upwelling of nutrient-rich water, for example in the Benguela Current off West Africa or in the Peruvian Humboldt Current. Zooplankton feeds on the phytoplankton and so the chain continues until it culminates in either large fishes or enormous numbers of seabirds, or both.

Some warm-water marine fishes are pelagic all their lives,

The main ocean currents of the world.

currents

and many shore species have pelagic young. The Herring (*Clupea harengus*), which feeds on zooplankton, concentrates in spawning grounds. When the larvae hatch they drift with the currents until they are large enough to swim into coastal nursery areas. On reaching maturity, they return to the spawning grounds. The young of the Common Pompano (*Trachinotus carolinas*) are frequently found in small schools along sandy shores of north-eastern America in the autumn. They are situated far north of the adult population, presumably having been carried by the northward drift of the current; on reaching a sufficient size they move south again.

pelagic fish

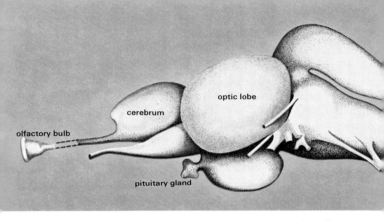

olfactory bulb

cerebrum

optic lobe

pituitary gland

In the brain of a fish areas associated with the sense of smell are particularly well developed.

Navigation

As a general rule, fishes on their way to breed swim against the current and after spawning move with the current. Cod certainly fit this rule, and Plaice clearly do the same. A population of Plaice (*Pleuronectes platessa*) in the inshore waters surrounding the Shetland Islands were found to move against the anti-clockwise current, and into this situation some Plaice were transferred from a region where they were moving clockwise. The introduced fishes moved with the established population against the current.

The means whereby fishes detect the current is not fully understood. A fish in a mass of moving water is in effect part of the body of water and will move with it, and will be unable to feel in which direction the current is moving. Regardless of any current the fish will sense a pressure on its head when it moves forward and only when the fish is being carried passively will this pressure be absent. So it can be assumed that sensing current by the same means that it senses forward movement is not likely to be an answer. In shallow-water conditions the story is different. Firstly, when in a stream or inshore habitat there is likely to be a different pressure of current at various levels, and this could cause the fish to tilt; this change of position would be detected by the inner ear. Also, when close to the bottom or in weeds, a fish would have some point of reference against which it could relate its own movement and hence the pressure of the current.

Following the principle of Kramer's experiments with Starlings fishes can be made to orientate by means of the sun, and change their position when they are influenced by an artificial sun. They can compensate exactly for variations in azimuth, and can maintain a constant direction. They can also detect the changes in height of the sun and could thereby know their latitude.

It is immediately noticeable on making a dissection of the brain of a fish that the olfactory centres are extremely large, and it has been shown that a fish has an acute olfactory sense. Pirañas, the South American cannibal fishes, gather instantly around a bleeding carcass, and sharks are attracted by bait even if they are some miles away. This sense could therefore be the clue to the accurate return made by salmon to their natal stream. If the acidity or mineral content, characteristic of a particular brook, were imprinted on the memory of a salmon then it could find its way back to it. This has been proved experimentally by damaging the olfactory senses of tagged salmon. At a division of the stream, roughly equal numbers of damaged salmon would take each turning, whereas when undamaged they chose their natal stream.

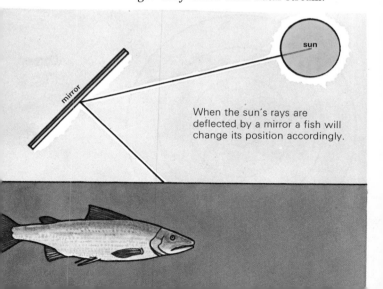

When the sun's rays are deflected by a mirror a fish will change its position accordingly.

MIGRATION OF INVERTEBRATES

If the strict definition of migration is upheld, then a large proportion of movements made by the vast numbers of simple animals are not true migrations. However, some are considered migratory and many of the animals are capable of orientation and return to their home: indeed some appear to possess accurate biological clocks.

Planarians are small, flat worms of very simple structure and are often found hidden under stones in streams. They are carnivorous, and in the laboratory can be made to react to small pieces of fresh meat. If a planarian is placed in a shallow dish of water and the bait is put in the centre, the planarian moves obliquely to it. By gradually moving forwards with side to side movements of the head, the worm gets closer until, after moving in a slight spiral, it reaches the centre. The reason for this behaviour is that the planarian

Planarian movements are guided by minute chemical stimuli.

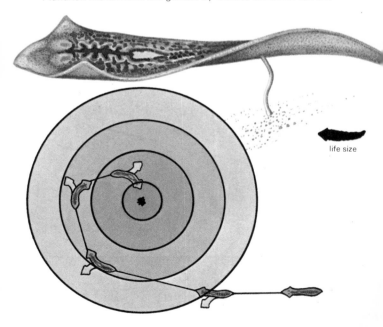

life size

possesses receptors which detect extremely minute quantities of chemicals, or 'scent', in the water, and it appears to measure the concentration towards the source and then away from it, so that there is an assessment by comparison. This kind of behaviour is fairly common in simple animals and possibly some of the molluscs use it to find food. These very simple movements are connected with migration only by the common factor of chemo-sensitivity.

Almost migratory are limpets, which at high tide move across the home rock surface to feed, and when the tide begins to fall return to their permanent rest site.

Another near migrant is the Palolo Worm (*Eunice viridis*) of the Pacific and Caribbean. During the last quarter of the moon of October and November, the Palolos breed, and in a short period of a few nights the worms divide and come to the surface in two halves – male and female. They are seen in great numbers and local people collect them for food.

Pacific islanders catch Palolo Worms when they surface to breed.

Sensitivity to odours reaches a high degree among insects. When one sees a long line of ants busily rushing along, they are following a trail laid down by others before them. The ants have various chemo-sensitive hairs on their antennae, and by using the antennae rather like a blind man might use a stick, they find their way by means of minute traces of chemicals, rather than just by recognizing the path by touch. It has been suggested that ants can detect the shape or size of an odour, and that trails possess a gradient of scent which helps them to determine the direction of travel.

If the trail is broken by wiping a finger across it, the ants rush up to the break and then rush back again in a confused state, but if the trail is wiped out with clean cotton wool, the ants cross the gap without stopping. This seems to indicate that the smear made by the finger contained some substance which was detectable and strange to the ants.

When ants move around they lay a trail of a chemical substance which other ants can detect, with special hairs, and follow.

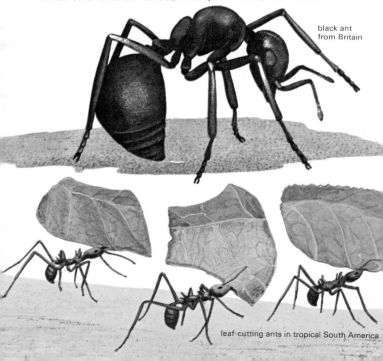

black ant
from Britain

leaf-cutting ants in tropical South America

For ants, scent-laying hardly constitutes navigation: it is a guide line laid down by those foragers which are successful in locating food. Once an ant with food returns to the nest, more and more ants follow the trail, thus reinforcing the scent. If the food supply decreases, the number of individuals making the journey diminishes and the trail begins to dry up. This drying up is thus related to the general decline of activity along the route and back in the nest. There are obvious advantages to this system, the main one being that foraging power is not wasted.

Although scent trails are not regarded as a form of navigation, insects and certain other arthropods can orientate by using the sun as a fixed point. Some insects have been shown to home on landmarks. For example, Tinbergen, working in Holland, demonstrated that Bee-wolfs (*Philanthus triangulum*) can recognize the small features surrounding the nest.

Sandhoppers (tiny crustaceans) occur in millions

Experiments have demonstrated that ants can determine their position relative to the sun.

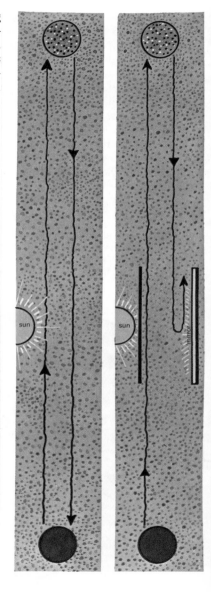

on the sandy beaches of Europe. They remain in the belt of wet sand above the powerful wash of the sea. If these hoppers are taken up the beach to the drier sand, they immediately make their way back to the wet zone. The orientation of these animals was studied by L. Pardi and F. Papi, Italian scientists. They reported that, if hoppers on the Adriatic coast were taken inland, they always returned to the sea, but, if hoppers from the same place were taken across country to the Mediterranean coast, they also moved eastward, which took them away from the sea. Further investigation revealed that the hoppers held their course by using the sun, and that they react to polarized light. However, they must also possess some compensation mechanism to allow for movement of the

Sandhoppers which had been kept in artificial day/night conditions (numbers inside circle) moved in a different direction to those hoppers not subjected to this treatment (numbers outside circle). The experiment demonstrates that an internal clock and a compensation mechanism are important in sandhopper orientation.

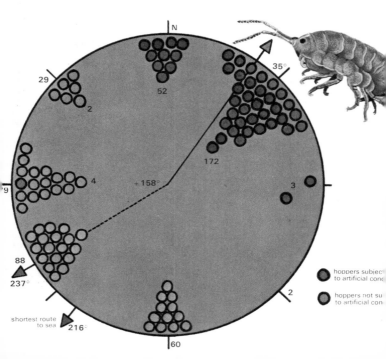

sun, and even for the movement of the moon, since the same sandhoppers were found to orientate on moon-lit nights.

Karl von Frisch investigated orientation by light in animals, mainly arthropods (the jointed limbed invertebrates with an external skeleton such as insects, crabs, and spiders). Generally the movements made by these animals are not migrations but wanderings, in search of food, for instance. They tend to move in a straight line by keeping an eye to the light. It has been suggested that this behaviour is more likely to bring the animal into contact with a fresh food supply, than is moving in a zig-zag.

Sometimes hordes of marine crabs make these one-way straight-line movements and long distances have been reported. Often the females leave the water after the breeding season, while the males remain behind, and sometimes seasonal drying of coastal lagoons causes a severe salinity change and thousands of crabs make for a new area. Usually nothing will deter such a mass movement. If something animate blocks their path, the leading crabs hesitate but are forced on by their followers. If they do take evasive action by moving sideways, they afterwards continue in exactly the same direction.

A mass movement of crabs in the coastal Caribbean region.

eyes

Uca uca

ladybird beetles

dragonfly

termites

Some insect migrants.

Among the familiar insect migrants are termites, butterflies, moths, locusts and dragonflies. In Europe large invasions of dragonflies have been seen and when one species (*Sympetrum striolatum*) invaded Ireland in 1947, the population almost certainly arrived from Spain and Portugal after a long flight over the sea. Other notable migrants are the Five-Spot Libellula (*Libellula maculata*), which has been recorded in millions in Heligoland, and another species (*Panatala flavescens*), which was recorded in the last century in the Pacific at least 300 miles from land.

The familiar ladybirds or coccinellid beetles migrate. For example, the Seven-Spot Ladybird (*Coccinella septempunctata*) moves regularly between summer and winter areas. Records of the migrations of ladybirds show that the numbers reach truly fantastic proportions. An estimated 4,500 million individuals have been recorded in one flight.

No single factor can account for the occasional swarms of such insects, but almost certainly the major factor is a good climate leading to an abundance of food, which in turn leads to overcrowding. This type of movement is termed 'density dependent' and it only occurs after the population reaches a certain density. Once the limit has been reached the movement occurs, and, although some species are known to follow definite directions, others move as freely as the clouds swirling about at the command of the wind. Greenfly take advantage of the winds to disperse from their breeding areas, and as gardeners know too well, in some years they are extremely numerous. They reproduce parthenogenetically, but the progeny are always female, and often wingless. In October the males appear and mate with the last generation of wingless females to produce a balanced male-female progeny. Far more colourful, but often as disastrous are the migrations of butterflies, and in this field the authoritative work of Dr C. B. Williams covers reports from all parts of the world, and provides a number of categories for the migrations.

Butterflies are familiar insect migrants.

Clouded Yellow

Long-tailed Blue

Red Admiral

Large White

Butterfly migrants can be listed in as many as nine groups, but more conveniently this list can be reduced to six. At the top are the species permanently resident in an area. These are followed by those species making only a short migration, those which are in passage only and do not breed and those in passage which do breed en route. Sometimes the permanent residents are reduced by emigration or reinforced by immigration.

The number of migrant species is very high and in America alone 250 have been identified. To check the extent of any of the migrations, a method of marking had to be devised and the problem was initially far greater than that encountered with birds or mammals. Some of the first attempts included marking the wings with punched holes or dye, but the butterfly is a very delicate creature and these methods were not entirely satisfactory. One of the most recent and widespread techniques for marking makes use of a small, light, self-adhesive, paper label which carries a number and is attached to the wings. This method has produced some good results, and one researcher in the United States has had recoveries reported from 1,200 miles away.

A tagged Monarch Butterfly and close-up of the tag.

The swarms of migrating butterflies reach enormous proportions. On one occasion in Kenya, in February 1926, a flight of *Belenois mesentina* was recorded. It was estimated that there were thirty-six million individuals for every mile of the swarm front. The migrants continued to pass the observer for fourteen days. From the Himalayas in mid-April 1919, a naturalist reported a migration of the Cabbage White (*Pieris brassicae*) and *Colias fieldi*. Hundreds were passing every minute. It was said that the hillside seemed covered with fluttering wings as the migrants moved slowly up the slope towards the snowline.

Unless blown by strong winds, migrating butterflies continue on a straight-line course, and obstructions do not deflect them. They have been seen flying up the wall of a house, over the roof and down the other side, and if the windows are open on both sides they pass through. In the same way, when confronted by a ravine, the line of butterflies winds down one side and up the other without a break. There are many variations in the type of movement, and many of these should not strictly be termed migrations. Most flights are one way and some are not periodic.

When long lines of butterflies are migrating, no low barrier will stop them.

The Painted Lady (*Vanessa virginiensis*) occurs in every continent except South America and has been reported from a wide range of unusual places. It has been seen in mid-Atlantic, in the north of Europe beyond the Arctic Circle, and in large numbers on its usual migration routes.

This butterfly is perhaps the greatest of all butterfly migrants, and wherever it occurs it is celebrated for incredible movements which coincide with particular times of the year. In the Palearctic Area (Europe and north and central Asia) there is a tendency for the movement to be towards the north and west. The life history of individuals found in Europe is simple. Eggs are laid in North African deserts, where they hatch when the spring rains bring short-lived greenery. The caterpillars feed and change into chrysalids. Then as soon as butterflies emerge the migration commences. By March or April they reach the Mediterranean, which they cross and move on northwards. Sometimes they breed a

The Painted Lady is one of the most famous butterfly migrants.

second time on the way, and in good years they are found in Britain and even further north.

In North America, the Painted Lady passes the winter in the semi-deserts of northern Mexico and in the spring the butterflies migrate north, spreading across the entire United States and into eastern Canada. It is another case of millions on the move at one time.

Painted Lady migrations have been reported from the Red Sea region and from many places in Asia, including the mountainous parts of Pakistan where they were seen at heights of 17,000 feet. The list of sightings is countless and yet in spite of the vast wealth of information, there are few authenticated records of what might be interpreted as a return flight. If there is no return flight, then it has to be assumed that all but a few of the migrants die with the onset of cold weather in the territories invaded. Possibly the movements are an invasion and not a migration, and in view of the enormous numbers which emerge in the breeding grounds it seems most likely that there is a major dispersal northward, following the progressively improving weather.

The main migration routes of the Painted Lady.

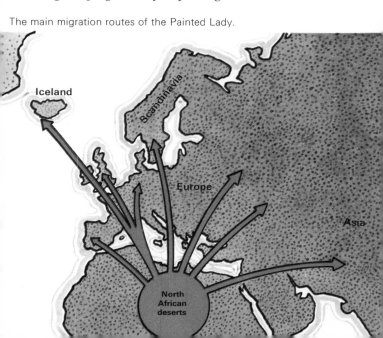

Perhaps the most famous and most colourful of the migrant butterflies is the Monarch or Milkweed (*Danaus plexippus*) of North America. Its life cycle is very closely related to the Milkweed plant on which it lays its eggs, since this is the principal food plant of the caterpillars. Although Monarchs have been recorded in Europe, they have failed to establish themselves there because of the absence of Milkweed. On the other hand the Monarch reached Hawaii in 1850, and pressed on westwards to colonize Borneo and New Zealand.

In the Americas there are two distinct populations (subspecies) of the Monarch: one occurs in the northern sub-continent and the other south of the Amazon. The latter sub-species differs from the northern one in that it lacks the black bar at the lower edge of the forewings. The migration patterns are different in the two groups.

At the onset of frosts in the northern parts of North America, Monarchs begin to disperse. Starting in their hundreds, they soon swell to

Monarch Butterfly and a
Milkweed plant.

a great flood of butterflies, moving day and night southwards through the United States. They fly up to 400 feet above the ground. For most butterflies twenty feet is the average.

The next stage is hibernation: the butterflies find a suitable place, usually settling on the branches and trunks of trees at sites used year after year. Occasionally the masses of butterflies are so dense that they become a great tourist attraction and reportedly their collective weight can break some of the branches. When spring arrives the richly coloured insects make their way northwards, but instead of favouring the gregarious pattern, characteristic of the southward migration, they move singly or in small groups. Monarchs breed at both ends of the migratory route and those individuals migrating northwards after hibernation do not make a second journey south again. This particular species has the ability to continue flying for immense distances, often apparently without directional instinct, which is one reason why it is at times found far from its normal haunts.

Monarch Butterfly migration routes in North America.

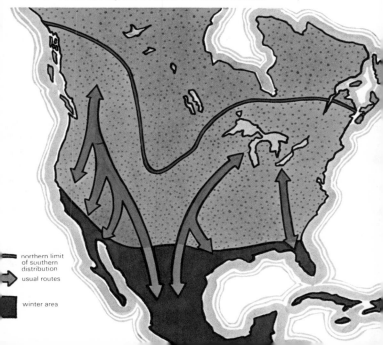

northern limit
of southern
distribution
usual routes

winter area

Death's Head Hawk Moth (left) and Bogong Moth.

Some moths are known migrants and possibly there are hundreds more migratory species, but there is a paucity of information due to the obvious difficulties facing the naturalist intent on studying the movements.

The Death's Head Hawk Moth (*Acherontia atropos*) which begins its journey in northern Africa and southern Europe gets its name from the skull-like markings on the upper thorax. Often the migrations made by this moth are extensive, and it has been seen as far afield as Iceland. More frequently it reaches as far as England and Scandinavia.

A moth (*Alabama argillacea*) of the southern United States is of considerable economic importance. Called the Cotton-worm, it invades the cotton fields between May and July to lay its eggs on cotton plants. The larvae, if uncontrolled, can defoliate thousands of acres. The insect arrives in the United States from South and Central America, but it appears only at intervals. Records of the invasions dating back to the late sixteenth century indicate that they have occurred with a remarkable periodicity of twenty-one or twenty-two years. After breeding for one or two generations, the moths die out, though the final stage sometimes includes a mass northward migration which has been known to reach Canada.

The Bogong Moth of south-east Australia belongs to a group which is spread world-wide. It is a migrant. In the spring it leaves the lower areas of cultivated land and moves into the mountains of New South Wales where it spends the summer months in a state of inanimation in caves, and then it returns to the plains in autumn.

When moths migrate, the numbers can be every bit as impressive as the great butterfly hordes. The shallow Portachuelo Pass in Venezuela is famous for massive moth migrations: William Beebe recorded that in certain seasons a mighty southward migration continued nightly. Capturing moths in these conditions is not difficult, but after marking, the chances of making a single recovery are very slight.

One of the best places in the world for collecting migrating moths is the famous Portachuelo Pass in Venezuela.

Orientation of Insects

Although there are exceptions, most insect migrations, including those of butterflies and moths, would seem to be more of a dispersal after breeding than true migrations. Generally the journeys are one way. Although they often cover the same route year after year, others are not much more than a swarm carried along with the wind. This type of movement requires very little, if any, ability to navigate, but it does demand some orientation mechanism to hold the flight direction without deviation.

The insect eye is referred to as a compound eye, since it is composed of many similar units or *ommatidia*, in each of which there is a number of light-sensitive cells packed around a central rod, the *rhabdome*. It is unlikely that the insect eye has great acuity, but at the same time it probably can detect movements and changes of intensity of light. Additionally, we know that the insect eye is sensitive to

1 Longitudinal section of an ommatidium of an insect compound eye. **2** Front view of a compound eye. **3** Cross-section of an ommatidium.

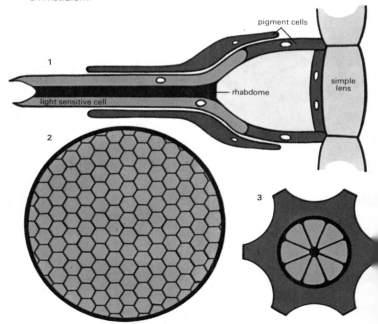

pigment cells

simple lens

rhabdome

light sensitive cell

1

2

3

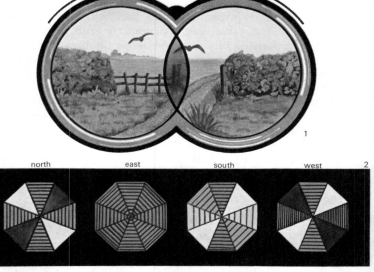

north   east   south   west   2

1 When two pola screens are revolved, a darkened area appears where they overlap. **2** When different parts of the sky are viewed through an artificial eye constructed of polarized glass different patterns are seen.

polarized light, and can detect the pattern of this light and hence the position of the sun, even when the sky is partially cloud-covered. If light is regarded as a wave travelling along a rope with the planes of vibration being in all directions and not just up and down, then if some light is reflected from a surface, only the vibrations in one direction are reflected. This is termed *plane polarized* light.

Light from the sun is not polarized until it reaches the particles in the outer atmosphere. Part of the light is then scattered, the pattern of polarization depending on the position of the sun. Some sunglasses are made of polarizing screen, and when the sky is viewed through them some areas seem darker than others; this is due to the variation in the polarization of the sky. When the two polarizing lenses are rotated until the planes of polarization are at right angles, then the light is cut out entirely as all planes of vibration are eliminated.

Von Frisch experimented with bees which, as he had previously discovered, can communicate with each other. When a polarizing filter was put above the bees they were disorientated but through the same angle as the shift of the light polarization. Von Frisch also made an octagon from eight pieces of polaroid glass set at different positions. This somewhat resembled the compound eye of an insect and indeed when the octagon was rotated the pattern changed, giving an effect similar to that which is probably experienced by the bees when they turn in scattered sunlight.

Of all the intriguing results from the experiments with bees, perhaps the most amazing is the answer to the question

After foraging, bees perform a complex dance in the hive.

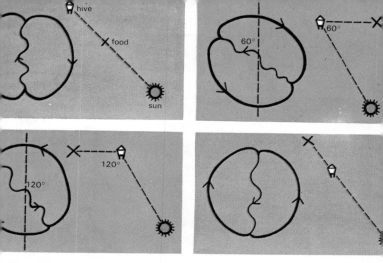

The direction of the bees' dance is related to the direction of the food source and the sun.

of communication. If the bees find a good source of nectar during their foraging, how can they pass this information to the other workers? Von Frisch discovered that the patterns danced by the foragers when they return to the hive are related to the position of the sun or the plane of polarized light, and in turn to the direction and distance of the food source from the hive. In this way, bees pass the vital information to other workers.

The dances are usually performed in complete darkness on the vertical face of the comb inside the hive, and to study them a special observation hive has to be constructed. There are certain general rules which apply to the dances, though distinct variations are apparent among different populations. The distance to the food is indicated by the speed of the dance. The greater the distance between the food source and the hive, the slower is the dance performed by the worker bee. If the dance is made at an angle to the vertical then this indicates that the bee must fly at that angle to the left or right of the sun. Some mystery remains, however: on one occasion the bees had to fly around the base of a hill to reach the food, and yet their dance showed the direct line route.

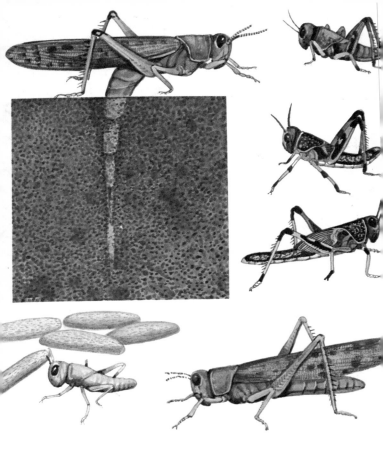

The life cycle of the locust. Probably such factors as wind and temperature affect the breeding cycle.

Von Frisch demonstrated that by changing the polarization of the light, the direction indicated by the dancers altered correspondingly.

Certain major characteristics of insect migration are fairly clear. Usually the flights are strongly in one direction without deviation or return, and the sun is important in maintaining the direction. However, the factors which determine the route, the goal and the time of departure have not been settled. Various suggestions have been put forward and these concern two categories of influencing factors, external and internal. Among the former are pressure and moisture gradients, wind, temperature and odours, and into the second category come instinct, biological clocks and perhaps some type of memory.

Some of the most searching studies have involved locusts. Although their swarming is generally not considered to be migration, the reasons why the phenomenon occurs seem to apply, in general terms, to many insect migrations.

Plagues of locusts have afflicted mankind for generations. They are mentioned in the Old Testament and more recent observers have given detailed descriptions. One swarm of Desert Locusts (*Schistocerca gregaria*) seen over the Red Sea in 1889 covered approximately 2,000 square miles and the weight was estimated at more than 3,000 tons. Evidence for swarming in the distant past comes occasionally from such unlikely places as the deep ice of glaciers.

North and South America have separate species of locust, and there are others in Africa and Asia. The worst havoc is caused by the depredations of the Desert Locust, which occurs from Africa through Arabia to India, and the Migratory Locust (*Locusta migratoria*) which is exclusively African. In 1921 Dr B. P. Uvarov proved that Migratory Locusts occur in two phases. Previously these were considered to be two

Masses of locusts preserved in glaciers provide evidence of swarming hundreds of years ago.

distinct species. During the solitary phase the locusts appear to exist in well-balanced equilibrium with their environment, then some stimulus causes the individuals to gather together. Possibly the climate and food supply are mainly responsible, and when the locusts swarm in an area rich with vegetation, two things happen: they begin to reduce the food supply quickly and they produce several generations in one summer. There are clearly defined differences between the solitary phase and the gregarious or migratory phase. The latter, for instance, is characterized by a higher metabolic rate and oxygen intake, associated with the increased activity, and by longer wings, shorter legs, and a darker brown colour.

In the autumn the female lays twenty to one hundred eggs, which remain in the ground until spring, when young hoppers hatch. They grow slowly, shedding two or three skins as they develop. If the overcrowding begins during the summer, millions of the gregarious phase are reared. Being active they begin to move and very quickly the ground is covered with a heaving, struggling mass of hoppers. Nothing stops them; they are hard to drown and even deliberate fires are smothered by their millions. When the hoppers develop wings and take to the air, locusts form their familiar clouds and move onwards to regions of good vegetation. All the time they continue to reproduce and the numbers swell to vast proportions, until eventually they outgrow the food supply and nearly all of them die. This entire cycle is thought to be a method of regulating the population so that the

Seasonal movements of the Desert Locust in Africa and southern Asia.

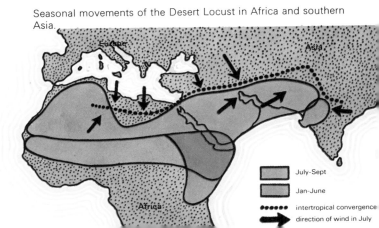

	July–Sept
	Jan–June
●●●●●●	intertropical convergence
➡	direction of wind in July

Although locust swarms are harmful to man, they provide food
for other animals including the Digger Wasp (inset) in Africa.

normal, balanced relationship between the locusts and their
food supply can be re-established.

Generally the movements of the Migratory Locust are
regarded as invasions and not migrations. The Desert Locust,
however, would seem to provide a better case for migratory
behaviour. The limits of the two breeding areas used each
year are determined by the position of the inter-tropical
convergence zone, a front, marking the boundary between
two opposing wind pressures. If locusts penetrate north of
the front in July, the winds push them back. Thus one might
argue that the locusts are merely at the whim of the wind.

A locust control unit in Africa.

APPLICATIONS OF MODERN RESEARCH

It is in situations of economic importance where the effects and nature of migrations are given most attention. Locusts have plagued farmers, especially, in some of the less wealthy parts of the world, and it has been necessary to establish a scientific programme to tackle the problems arising when biology is mixed with economics. A central organization is the Anti Locust Research Centre based in London, which receives information from affected regions. All kinds of data are collected, from detailed climate reports to studies of genetics and physiology. By sifting through information gathered over a long period, it is possible that some features of locust behaviour may stand out, and studying these could possibly lead to methods of control, or more accurate long-range forecasting of locust invasions.

Similarly the studies of fish migration are of vital importance today, if man is to utilize the oceans wisely. It is not much use if overfishing in a particular ground is misinterpreted as an absence of fishes due to their moving away. It is also essential that the fishermen should know how many fishes they can take before the natural ecological balance is upset. Fisheries research is conducted by many countries and some of the projects could have far-reaching effects. Recently Peru has advanced to the top of the world's fishing charts as a major producer on a level with Japan. The Humboldt Current is rich in the Anchovy which is used for making fishmeal, but there is some doubt about the status of the Anchovy after heavy fishing or at times when the Humboldt Current is upset. Research has indicated that there are two main populations of Anchovy, but the movements of these are uncertain. If more were known there could possibly be some benefit for the economics of the industry. To check on the migrations, a tagging programme has been started, and small magnetic tags are now inserted into the skin of the fishes. Several million will have been tagged by the time that the programme is completed, and hopefully just a few tags will be recorded by detectors in the fishmeal plants. Tag numbers, location dates and other data might lead to a useful discovery and so our knowledge of animal migrations will advance another step.

An Anchovy fishmeal factory in Peru.

BOOKS TO READ

Animal Migration by Otto von Frisch. Collins, London, 1969
Animal Navigation by J. D. Carthy. Unwin Books, London, 1963
Bird Migration by Donald R. Griffin. Heinemann, London, 1964
Bird Navigation by G. V. T. Matthews. Cambridge University
    Press, Cambridge, 1968
Insect Migration by C. B. Williams. Collins, London, 1965
Locusts and Grasshoppers by B. P. Uvarov. Cambridge University
    Press, Cambridge, 1928
Ornithology: An Introduction by Austin L. Rand. Signet Science
    Library, 1969
Seals of the World by Gavin Maxwell, John Stidworthy and
    David Williams. Constable, London, 1967
The Dancing Bees by Karl von Frisch. Methuen, London, 1954
The Migrations of Birds by Jean Dorst. Heinemann, London, 1962
The Migration of Butterflies by C. B. Williams. Oliver, Edinburgh,
    1930
The Mystery of Animal Migration by Matthieu Ricard. Constable,
    London, 1969

PLACES TO VISIT

Bardsey Island Bird and Field Observatory, Aberdaron, North
    Wales
Calf of Man Bird Observatory, Isle of Man
Cape Clear Bird Observatory, County Cork, Eire
Copeland Bird Observatory, Northern Ireland
Dungeness Bird Observatory, Romney Marsh, Kent
Fair Isle Bird Observatory, Shetland
Gibraltar Point Bird Observatory and Field Station, Skegness,
    Lincolnshire
Holme Bird Observatory, Hunstanton, Norfolk
Isle of May Bird Observatory and Field Station, Fife
Portland Bird Observatory and Field Centre, Dorset
Sandwich Bay Bird Observatory, Kent
Spurn Bird Observatory, Kilnsea, via Patrington, Hull, East
    Yorkshire
Walney Bird Observatory, Walney Island, Lancashire

INDEX

Page numbers in bold type
refer to illustrations.

Acherontia atropus 144,
144
Agelaius phoeniceus 54
Alabama argillacea 144
Albatross 24
Black-browed **58**, 59
Laysan **68**, 90, **90**
Anadromous fishes 118
Anas discors 67
platyrhynchos 96, **96**
Anchovy 12, 155, **155**
Anguilla anguilla 124, 125,
125
rostrata 125
Anser albifrons 46
anser 46
brachyrhynchus 46
coerulescens coerulescens
66, **66**, 67
fabialis 46
Ant 132, 133, **133**
black **132**
leaf-cutting **132**
Antidorcas marsupialis 11,
35, **35**
Apus apus 4
Aquila pomarina 45
Asio flammeus 24, **24**

Balaenoptera physalus 36
Banding *see* Ringing
Bass, Striped **121**
Bat 39, **39**
brown 39
Grey-headed Flying Fox
39, **39**
Large Mouse-eared 39
Bear, Polar 37, **37**
Bee 148–150, **148**, **149**
Bee-wolf 133
Beebe, William 145
Belenois mesentina 139
Biological clock 104–107
104, 109, 112, 130, **134**
Bison 34, **35**
Bison bison 34, **35**
Biziura lobata 87
Blackbird, Red-winged 54
Blackcap 108, 109
Bobolink **74**, 75
Bombycilla garrulus 8
Breeding cycle 10, 102
Brevoortia tyrannus 121,
121

Bubulcus ibis 18, **18**, **19**
Bunting 49
Indigo 48, **49**, 106, **106**,
107
Snow **40**
Butterfly 7, 137–143, **139**,
146
Cabbage White 139
Clouded Yellow **137**
Large White **137**
Long-tailed Blue **137**
Milkweed *see* Monarch
Monarch **138**, 142, **142**,
143, **143**
Painted Lady 140, **140**,
141, 141
Red Admiral **137**
Buzzard, Honey 45, **77**

Calidris acuminata 51
bairdii 42
ferruginea 41, **43**
maritima 42
mauri 70
Callorhinus ursinus 37, 38,
38
Cannon net 61, **61**
Caribou 32, 33
Carmargue 81
Carr, Dr Archie 115
Catadomous fishes 118
Celestial navigation 106,
107, **107**, 109, 113, 117
Cervus canadensis 22
Chaimarrornis leucocephalus
54, 55
Charadrius semipalmatus 75
Chemo-sensitivity 129,
131, 132, **132**
Chloephaga poliocephala
43, 46
Chrysococcyx lucidus 51
Ciconia ciconia 4, 42
Clupea harengus 127
Coccinella septempunctata
136
Cod 120, **120**, **121**, 128
Colias fieldi 139
Collocalia esculenta 25, **25**
Colonization 27, 30
Condor, Andean 23, **23**, 63
63
Continental drift 16, **16**
Coot 48, **48**, **49**
Coriolis Force 101, **102**
Corvus corone cornix 98
99
Cottonworm 144

Coturnix coturnix 6
Courser, Cream-coloured
26
Cowbird 54
Crab 135, **135**
Crake 49
Corn- 49
Spotted 49
Crane **5**, 6, 44, **44**
Crex crex 49
Crossbill **26**, 27
Crow, Hooded 98, **99**
Cuckoo 4, 98, **98**
Bronze 51
Long-tailed 51, **51**
Cuculus canorus 4
Curlew, Bristle-thighed 78,
79
Cygnus buccinator 47
columbianus 47
melancoriphus 46, **46**,
47

Danaus plexippus 142, **142**,
143, **143**
Danube Delta 81
Day length 103
Deer, Guemal *see* Taruga
North American *see*
Wapiti
Density dependent move-
ment 136, 137
Diomedea immutabilis 90,
90
melanophris **58**, 59
Diver, Great Northern **46**,
47
Dolichonyx oryzivorous **74**,
75
Dragonfly 136, **136**
Duck **47**, 86
Common Eider 71
Garganey 41
Mallard 96, **96**
Musk 87
Old Squaw **40**
Steamer 87
Stiff-tailed 87
Dyeing 59, **59**, 138

Eagle, Lesser Spotted 45
Short-toed **77**
Echo-location 39
Eel **124**
American 125
European 124, 125, **125**
Egret, Cattle 18, **18**, **19**

Electric light 63
Emlen, S.T. 106, **106**, 107
Engraulis encrasicolus 12
Eschrichtius glaucus 36, 37
Eunice viridis 131, **131**

Falco peregrinus 69, **69**
Falcon, Peregrine 69, **69**
  Red-footed 45
Fish, Blue 121
Flight paths of birds 76, **76**, 77
Flycatcher 41
  Sulphur-bellied **74**
Frog 116, 117, **117**

Gadus morhua 120, **120**, **121**
Gannet **68**, 95, **95**
Gavia immer **46**, 47
Gnu **34**
Godwit, Bar-tailed 78
Goose 46
  Ashy-headed 43, 46
  Bean **40**, 46, **86**
  Blue 66, **66**, 67
  Canada **46**
  Greylag 46, 61
  White-fronted 46
Grackle 54
  Common **54**
Great Ice Age 14, **14**
Grebe, Great Crested **42**
Ground Tyrant, Rufous-
  backed **74**
Gull, Herring **68**, 97
  Lesser Black-backed 79
Gypaetus barbatus 54

Halcyon sancta 73
Halichoerus grypus 38, **39**
Hawk Mountain Sanctuary
  80, **80**
Heligoland Trap **60**, 61
Heron, Grey **42**
  Purple **26**
Herring 127
Hippocamelus antisensis
  23
Hirundo rustica 4, 84, **84**
  85, **85**
  tahitica neoxena 85, 86
Hormones 102, 103
Hummingbird, Green-
  backed Firecrown 72
  Ruby-throated **11**

Ibisbill **55**

Inherited Migratory
  behaviour 97, 98, **98**
Invasion 11, 27, 153

Jay, Blue **42**

King Bird, Grey **74**
Kingfisher, Sacred **11**, 73
Kramer, Gustav 111, 112, **112**

Ladybird 136, **136**
  Seven-spot 136
Lammergeyer 54
Landmarks 94, **94**, 95, **95**, 113, 133
Lapwing, European 26, **26**
Larus fuscus 79
Laticauda spp. 116
Lemming 4, 11, 20–22, 20, **21**
  Arctic 21, **21**
  forest 21, **21**
Leopard, Snow 22, **22**
Libellula, Five-spot 136
Libellula maculata 136
Limosa lapponica* 78
Limpet 131
Locust 5, **150**, 151, **151**, **153**, 154, **154**
  Desert 151, **152**, 153
  Migratory 151–153
Loon 47

Mackerel 119
Magnetic field, Earth's
  100, **100**, 112
Martin, Brown Chested **74**
Matthews, Dr G. V. T. 96, **96**, 112, 113
Megalornis grus 5, 6, 44, **44**
Megaptera novaeangliae
  36, **36**
Menhaden 121, **121**
Microcephalophis spp. 116
Migratory restlessness 103
Migratory tribes 28, 29, **29**
Moose 56
Moth 144–146, **145**
  Bogong 144, **144**, 145
  Death's Head Hawk 144, **144**
Mutton Bird, Tasmanian
  see Short-tailed Shear-
  water
Myotis spp. 39
  myotis 39
*Myoxocephalus
  octodecemspinosus* 121

Nile Delta 81
Nonsense orientation 96
  96, 97
Numenius tahitiensis 78, **79**

Observation points 80, **80**, 81, **81**
Ocean currents 126, **126**, 127, **127**
Oceanites oceanicus **74**, 75
Oceanodroma leucorhoa 89
Oenanthe oenanthe 50, **50**
Oncorhynchus gorbuscha
  123
Oreortyx pictus 54, **55**
Osprey **11**, 45
Otus spp. 48
  scops 48
Owl, Scops 48
  Scops, European 48, **48**
  Screech *see* Scops
  Short-eared 24

Panatala flavescens 136
Pandion haliaetus 45
Pecten 109, **109**
Pelamis platurus **116**
Penguin, Adelie 90, 91, **91**
  King **27**
  Magellan 79
Pernis apivorus 45
Petrel, Leach's **68**, 89
  Wilson's **74**, 75
Petrochelidon pyrrhonata
  67
Phalaenoptilus nuttallii 55, **55**
Phalarope, Red-necked **27**
  Wilson's 9, **9**
Phalaropus tricolor 9, **9**
Phylloscopus sibilatrix 69
Pieris brassicae 139
Pigeon, homing 92, **92**
Plaice 128
Planarian 130, 131
Planetarium 107, **107**, 109
Pleuronectes platessa 128
Plover 69
  Black-bellied 75
  Caspian **27**
  Lesser Golden 51, **74**, **79**, 98, **98**
  Semi-palmated 75
  Slender-billed 72
Pluvialis dominica 51
  squatarola 75

Pluvianellus socialis 72
Polaris star 107–109, **108**
Polarized light 147, **147**, 148–150
Pompano, Common 127
Poor-will 55, **55**
Portachuelo Pass 81
Porzana porzana 49
Pteropus poliocephalus 39, **39**
Puffinus puffinus **68**, 88, **88**, 89, **89**
tenuirostris 78, **78**, **79**
Pygoscelis adeliae 90, 91, **91**

Quail 6
Mountain 54, **55**

Radar 62, **62**
'angels' 62
Radio transmitters 56, 62, 63, **63**, 115
Rail 49
Recovery 60, **60**, 61, **61**
Redstart, White-capped Water 54, 55
Reindeer 32, **32**, **33**
Ringing 7, 58, **58**, 59
Robin, American 45
Rorqual, Common 36
Ruff **26**

Saiga **32**, 33
Saiga tatarica 32, 33
Salamanca Island 81, **81**
Salmo salar 4, 122, 123
Salmon 4, 122, **122**, 123. **123**
Atlantic 122
King **122**
Pacific 122
Pacific Pink 123
Silver **122**
Stealhead Trout **122**
Sanderling **41**, **74**
Sandhopper 134, **134**
Sandpiper 69
Baird's 42
Curlew 41, **43**
Purple 42
Siberian Pectoral 51
Solitary 41, **43**
Western 71
Sauer, Dr F. 108, 109
Scomber scombrus 119

Sculpin, Long-horned 121
Seal 38
Atlantic *see* Grey
Grey 38, 39
Northern Fur *see* Pribilof Fur
Pribilof Fur 37, 38, **38**
Seasnake 116, **116**
Seasonal changes 29
Sephanoides sephanoides 72
Sextant 110, **111**
Shearwater, Manx **68**, 88, **88**, 89, **89**
Short-tailed 78, **78**, 79, 105, **105**
Slender-billed *see* Short-tailed
Sooty **74**
Shrike, Red-backed 45
Sibbaldus musculus 36
Site tenacity 91
Skimmer, Black **43**
Snare **60**, 61
Somateria mollissima 71
Southern Ancestral Home Theory 15
Sparrow, Vesper **54**
Spheniscus magellanicus 79
Spoon-bill **11**
Springbok 11, 35, **35**
Starling 10, 68, 82, **82**, 83, **83**, **97**, 111, 112, **112**
Sterna fuscata 105
paradisaea 52, **52**, 53, **53**
Stork, White 4, 42, **77**
Wood **26**
Sturnus vulgaris 82, **82** 83, **83**
Suicidal movements 11, 20, **20**, 21, **21**
Sula bassana 95, **95**
Sun navigation 110–113, **110**, **112**, **113**, 129, **129**, 133–135, **133**
Swallow 4, 9, 10, 41, 61, 64, **68**, 84, **84**, 85, **85**
Barn 84, **84**, 85, **85**
Cliff 67
Welcome 85, 86
Swan, Black-necked 46, **46**, 47
Trumpeter 47
Whistling 47
Swift 4, 9, 25, **25**, 41, 45, 64, **64**
Spine-tailed **11**
Sylvia atricapilla 108, 109
borin 108, 109
communis 109
Sympetrum striolatum 136

Tagging 138, **138**
Taruga 23
Teal, Blue-winged 67
Termite 136, **136**
Tern **68**
Arctic 52, **52**, 53, **53**, 67
Common **97**
Sooty 105
Territorial expansion 18, **18**, 19, **19**
Thalarctos maritimus 37, **37**
Thrush 49
Grey-cheeked **48**, **49**, **67**
Swainson's **48**, **49**
Tichodroma muraria 55
Tinbergen, N. 133
Toad 116, 117, **117**
Trachinotus carolinas 127
Tringa flavipes 67
solitaria 41, **43**
Tucker, Dr D. W. 125
Turtle 114–116, **114**, **115**
Green 114
Kemp's Loggerhead 114

Uca uca **135**
Uncia uncia 22, **22**
Urodynamis taitensis 51, **51**

Vanellus vanellus 26, **26**
Vanessa virginiensis 140 **140**, 141, **141**
Veery **48**, **49**
Vireo, Red-eyed **74**
Von Frisch, Karl 135, 148–150
Vulture, Bearded *see* Lammergeyer
Vultur gryphus 23, **23**

Wallcreeper 55
Wapiti 22
Warbler 41
Garden 108, 109
Wood **41**, 69
Waxwing 8
Whale 36
Blue 36
Californian Gray 36, 37
Humpback 36, **36**
Wheatear 50
Common 50, **50**
Whitethroat 109
Williams, Dr C.B. 137
Worm, Palolo 131, **131**
Wren 49

Yellowlegs, Lesser 67

SOME OTHER TITLES IN THIS SERIES

■ Arts   ■ General Information

■ Domestic Animals and Pets   ■ History and Mythology

■ Domestic Science   ■ Natural History

■ Gardening   ■ Popular Science

Arts
Antique Furniture/Architecture/Clocks and Watches/Glass for Collectors/Jewellery/Musical Instruments/Porcelain/Victoriana

Domestic Animals and Pets
Budgerigars/Cats/Dog Care/Dogs/Horses and Ponies/Pet Birds/Pets for Children/Tropical Freshwater Aquaria/Tropical Marine Aquaria

Domestic Science
Flower Arranging

Gardening
Chrysanthemums/Garden Flowers/Garden Shrubs/House Plants/ Plants for Small Gardens/Roses

General Information
Aircraft/Arms and Armour/Coins and Medals/Flags/Guns/Military Uniforms/National Costumes of the world/Rockets and Missiles/ Sailing/Sailing Ships and Sailing Craft/Sea Fishing/Trains/Veteran and Vintage Cars/Warships

History and Mythology
Age of Shakespeare/Archaeology/Discovery of: Africa/The American West/Australia/Japan/North America/South America/Myths and Legends of: Africa/Ancient Egypt/Ancient Greece/Ancient Rome/ India/The South Seas/Witchcraft and Black Magic

Natural History
The Animal Kingdom/Animals of Australia and New Zealand/ Animals of Southern Asia/Bird Behaviour/Birds of Prey/Butterflies/ Evolution of Life/Fishes of the world/Fossil Man/A Guide to the Seashore/ Life in the Sea/Mammals of the world/Monkeys and Apes/Natural History Collecting/The Plant Kingdom/Prehistoric Animals/Seabirds/Seashells/Snakes of the world/Trees of the World/Tropical Birds/Wild Cats

Popular Science
Astronomy/Atomic Energy/Chemistry/Computers at Work/The Earth/Electricity/Electronics/Exploring the Planets/The Human Body/Mathematics/Microscopes and Microscopic Life/Undersea Exploration/The Weather Guide